Edexcel GCSE

Mathematics B Modular Practice Book Targeting A and A*

Series Director: Keith Pledger
Series Editor: Graham Cumming

Authors:
Julie Bolter
Gareth Cole
Gill Dyer
Michael Flowers
Karen Hughes
Peter Jolly
Joan Knott
Jean Linsky
Graham Newman
Rob Pepper
Joe Petran
Keith Pledger
Rob Summerson
Kevin Tanner
Brian Western

About this book

Welcome to Edexcel's Practice Book for targeting A and A*!

If you've got this book, you're aiming for an A or A* in GCSE Maths – well done! You want to get those A and A* grade exam questions right though and that means you need to practise. Sometimes it is difficult to find enough questions at this level to practise on so we've made sure that this book gives you just that. It follows the order of your Higher Student Books but it does not include every chapter – we've picked out just those chapters with the most scope for A and A* questions and focused on those.

Key Points summaries recap the content and give you links between different areas of the specification

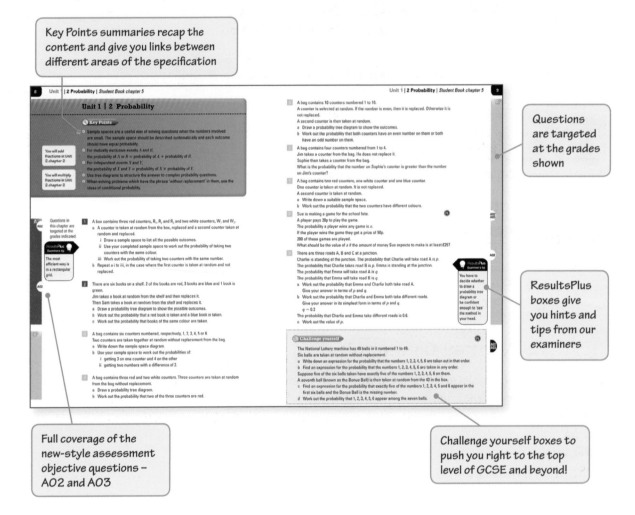

Questions are targeted at the grades shown

ResultsPlus boxes give you hints and tips from our examiners

Full coverage of the new-style assessment objective questions – AO2 and AO3

Challenge yourself boxes to push you right to the top level of GCSE and beyond!

Answers

Your teacher can access the answers at www.edexcelmaths.com/supportplus They will need to register and we will check that they are a teacher before giving them access to the answers! They may choose to give you the answers to mark your own work or they may mark it for you.

About this book

Assessment objectives

There are three **Assessment Objectives** which define the types of questions you get in the exam. There are different percentages of marks available for each of these.

Assessment Objective	What it is	What this means	Range % of marks in the exam
A01	**Recall** and use knowledge of the prescribed content.	Standard questions testing your knowledge of each topic.	45–55
A02	**Select** and apply mathematical methods in a range of contexts.	Deciding what method you need to use to get to the correct solution to a problem.	25–35
A03	**Interpret** and analyse problems and generate strategies to solve them.	Solving problems by deciding how and explaining why.	15–25

We have marked A02 and A03 questions so you can make sure that you can answer these as well as the A01 questions.

Functional mathematics

20–30% of marks in the Higher paper are for answering **functional mathematics** questions. These are questions about how to apply maths in everyday, real-life situations. We have marked these too so you can check how you are getting on with them.

Quality of Written Communication

There are also marks available for Quality of Written Communication. This means showing your working 'properly' and explaining your answers clearly. In the exam paper, such questions will be marked with a star (*) so we've marked questions that would be likely to carry these marks in this book in the same way so you can practise.

You need to:

◉ use the correct mathematical notation and vocabulary, to show that you can communicate effectively

◉ organise the relevant information logically.

When answering A and A* level questions, you often need to work through many stages to get to the answer so how you show your working is going to be especially important. Don't forget that this is not just for questions marked with a star – almost all questions carry method marks which you will lose if you don't show what you have done.

Contents

Unit 1 | 1 Processing, representing and interpreting data

Key Points

○ The area of a pie chart represents the total data.

○ When there are unequal class intervals on a histogram you adjust the height by using a scale of frequency density rather than width, where

$$\text{frequency density} = \frac{\text{frequency}}{\text{class width}}$$

or frequency = frequency density $\times$ class width.

○ The area of each bar on a histogram gives its frequency.

○ When there are n values of data then quartiles can be estimated from a cumulative frequency graph.

○ The estimate for the lower quartile is the $\frac{n+1}{4}$ th value.

○ The estimate for the median is the $\frac{n+1}{2}$ th value.

○ The estimate for the upper quartile is the $\frac{3n+1}{4}$ th value.

---

1   The table shows the maximum wind speeds on Hilbre Island, UK in December 2008.

Wind speed (w mph)	Days
$5 < w \leqslant 15$	2
$15 < w \leqslant 20$	8
$20 < w \leqslant 25$	6
$25 < w \leqslant 35$	8
$35 < w \leqslant 50$	7

a   Draw a histogram for the data in the table.

Moderate winds are between 13 mph and 18 mph.

b   Use your histogram to estimate the number of days of moderate wind.

c   Copy and complete the cumulative frequency table.

Wind speed (w mph)	Cumulative frequency (days)
$5 < w \leqslant 15$	
$15 < w \leqslant 20$	
$20 < w \leqslant 25$	
$25 < w \leqslant 35$	
$35 < w \leqslant 50$	

d   Draw a cumulative frequency graph.

e   Use your graph to estimate the:

   i median   **ii** lower and upper quartiles   **iii** interquartile range.

Gale force winds are between 39 mph and 54 mph.

f   Use your graph to estimate the number of days of gale force winds.

Questions in this chapter are targeted at the grades indicated.

Calculate the frequency density for each class.

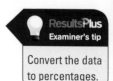

Convert the data to percentages.

2 The histogram shows the file sizes of 25 animal screensavers (in MegaBytes, MB)

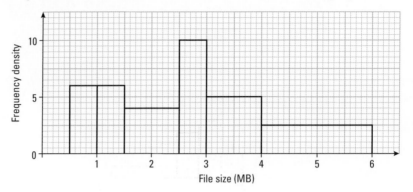

a Make a table of data.

The file sizes of 25 fantasy screensavers are shown below.

1.1   1.6   1.9   2.0   2.0   2.1   2.4   2.5   2.7   2.7   2.8   2.9   3.3

3.4   3.6   3.6   3.6   4.0.   4.5   6.2   7.3   8.6   9.8   10.3   14.6

b Make a table for the data, using 6 classes.

c Draw a histogram for the data.

Use estimates from your histogram to answer the following questions.

d How many **i** animal **ii** fantasy screensavers have a file size between 2.5MB and 4.5MB?

e Compare the number of animal and fantasy screensavers that larger than 4.5MB.

3 A main Post Office recorded the weights of parcels posted during a day.
The histogram illustrates the data.

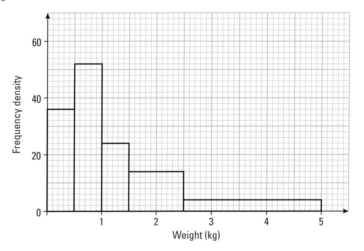

a Make a table for the data.

b Estimate the **i** mean **ii** median **iii** interquartile range.

4 Matthew sponsored a cheetah called Sheba and downloaded this histogram from the internet.

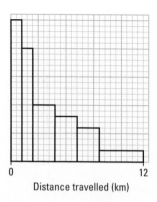

Distance travelled (km)

It shows the distances Sheba travelled each day for 50 days.
Make a table for the data.

> **Challenge yourself**

1 The broadband speeds of 60 households were recorded in each of three towns.
The diagrams show the data.

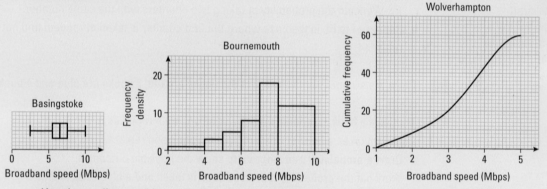

a Use the medians and interquartile ranges to compare the broadband speeds of the towns.

b Draw two different diagrams to illustrate the data for
  i Bournemouth
  ii Wolverhampton.

c **i** Combine the data for Bournemouth and Wolverhampton into a single table.
  ii Illustrate the combined data using three diagrams.

d **i** Find the average broadband speed for your school.
  ii Compare this speed with the combined data for the three towns.

Unit 1 | 2 Probability

Key Points

You will add fractions in Unit 2 chapter 2

○ Sample spaces are a useful way of solving questions when the numbers involved are small. The sample space should be described systematically and each outcome should have equal probability.

○ For mutually exclusive events A and B,
the probability of A or B = probability of A + probability of B.

You will multiply fractions in Unit 2 chapter 2

○ For independent events X and Y,
the probability of X and Y = probability of $X \times$ probability of Y.

○ Use tree diagrams to structure the answer to complex probability questions.

○ When solving problems which have the phrase 'without replacement' in them, use the ideas of conditional probability.

A

A02

Questions in this chapter are targeted at the grades indicated.

ResultsPlus
Examiners tip

The most efficient way is in a rectangular grid.

A02

1 A box contains three red counters, R_1, R_2 and R_3 and two white counters, W_1 and W_2.

  a A counter is taken at random from the box, replaced and a second counter taken at random and replaced.

    i Draw a sample space to list all the possible outcomes.

    ii Use your completed sample space to work out the probability of taking two counters with the same colour.

    iii Work out the probability of taking two counters with the same number.

  b Repeat **a i** to **iii**, in the case where the first counter is taken at random and not replaced.

2 There are six books on a shelf. 2 of the books are red, 3 books are blue and 1 book is green.

Jim takes a book at random from the shelf and then replaces it.

Then Sam takes a book at random from the shelf and replaces it.

  a Draw a probability tree diagram to show the possible outcomes.

  b Work out the probability that a red book is taken and a blue book is taken.

  c Work out the probability that books of the same colour are taken.

A*

3 A bag contains six counters numbered, respectively, 1, 2, 3, 4, 5 or 6.

Two counters are taken together at random without replacement from the bag.

  a Write down the sample space diagram.

  b Use your sample space to work out the probabilities of:

    i getting 3 on one counter and 4 on the other

    ii getting two numbers with a difference of 2.

4 A bag contains three red and two white counters. Three counters are taken at random from the bag without replacement.

  a Draw a probability tree diagram.

  b Work out the probability that two of the three counters are red.

5 A bag contains 10 counters numbered 1 to 10.
   A counter is selected at random. If the number is even, then it is replaced. Otherwise it is not replaced.
   A second counter is then taken at random.
   a Draw a probability tree diagram to show the outcomes.
   b Work out the probability that both counters have an even number on them or both have an odd number on them.

6 A bag contains four counters numbered from 1 to 4.
   Jim takes a counter from the bag. He does not replace it.
   Sophie then takes a counter from the bag.
   What is the probability that the number on Sophie's counter is greater than the number on Jim's counter?

7 A bag contains two red counters, one white counter and one blue counter.
   One counter is taken at random. It is not replaced.
   A second counter is taken at random.
   a Write down a suitable sample space.
   b Work out the probability that the two counters have different colours.

8 Sue is making a game for the school fete.
   A player pays 20p to play the game.
   The probability a player wins any game is x.
   If the player wins the game they get a prize of 50p.
   200 of these games are played.
   What should be the value of x if the amount of money Sue expects to make is at least £25?

A02
A03

9 There are three roads A, B and C at a junction.
   Charlie is standing at the junction. The probability that Charlie will take road A is p.
   The probability that Charlie takes road B is p. Emma is standing at the junction.
   The probability that Emma will take road A is q.
   The probability that Emma will take road B is q.
   a Work out the probability that Emma and Charlie both take road A.
      Give your answer in terms of p and q.
   b Work out the probability that Charlie and Emma both take different roads.
      Give your answer in its simplest form in terms of p and q.
      $q = 0.2$
   The probability that Charlie and Emma take different roads is 0.6.
   c Work out the value of p.

A02

ResultsPlus
Examiner's tip

You have to decide whether to draw a probability tree diagram or be confident enough to 'see' the method in your head.

> **Challenge yourself**

A02
A03

The National Lottery machine has 49 balls in it numbered 1 to 49.
Six balls are taken at random without replacement.
a Write down an expression for the probability that the numbers 1, 2, 3, 4, 5, 6 are taken out in that order.
b Find an expression for the probability that the numbers 1, 2, 3, 4, 5, 6 are taken in any order.
Suppose five of the six balls taken have exactly five of the numbers 1, 2, 3, 4, 5, 6 on them.
A seventh ball (known as the Bonus Ball) is then taken at random from the 43 in the box.
c Find an expression for the probability that exactly five of the numbers 1, 2, 3, 4, 5 and 6 appear in the first six balls and the Bonus Ball is the missing number.
d Work out the probability that 1, 2, 3, 4, 5, 6 appear among the seven balls.

Unit 2 | 3 Number (1)

Key Points

○ Any positive whole number, apart from 1, can be expressed as a product of its prime factors.

○ The Highest Common Factor (HCF) of two numbers m and n is the largest number that is a factor of both m and n.

You need this when you add and subtract fractions

○ The Lowest Common Multiple (LCM) of two numbers m and n is the smallest number that is a multiple of both m and n.

○ The index laws:

You use these in algebra (see section 1.4)

$$a^n \times a^m = a^{n+m} \qquad\qquad a^n \div a^m = a^{n-m}$$

$$a^{-n} = \frac{1}{a^n} \qquad\qquad a^0 = 1 \qquad (a^n)^m = a^{nm}$$

A
A02

Questions in this chapter are targeted at the grades indicated.

1 The diagram shows that $1 + 3 + 5 = 3^2 = 9$

Find the sum of all the odd numbers from 1 to 99 inclusive.

A02

2 Work out how many numbers less than or equal to 1000 are multiples of 3 or 5

3 $N = 168^5$
Write N^2 as a product of its prime factors.

4 Work out $2^{(2^3)} \div (2^2)^3$.

A☆
A02

5 For positive integer values of n, explain why one of the pair of numbers
$2^n - 1, \, 2^n + 1$
is divisible by 3

6 $x = pq$ and $y = rq$,
where p, q and r are prime numbers.
a Find the Highest Common Factor of x and y.
b Find the Lowest Common Multiple of x and y.

7 $m = p^4q$ and $n = p^2q^2$, where p and q are prime numbers.
a Find the Highest Common Factor of m and n. Give your answer in terms of p and q.
b Find the Lowest Common Multiple of m and n. Give your answer in terms of p and q.

A*

8 The Highest Common Factor of two numbers is 18. The Lowest Common Multiple of the same two numbers is 270. One of the numbers is 54.
Find the other number.

9 The Highest Common Factor of two numbers is 24. The Lowest Common Multiple of the same two numbers is 720.
Find all possible pairs of numbers.

* 10 For any two numbers m and n, let the Highest Common Factor be x and the Lowest Common Multiple be y.
Explain why $mn = xy$.

A03

11 $10^{10^{10}}$ can be written as an ordinary number.
a How many zeroes will it have at the end?
Let $x = 100$.
b How many zeroes will there be at the end of x^{x^x} when written as an ordinary number?
Give your answer as a power of 10.

> **Challenge yourself**

1 $n!$ means the product of all whole numbers from 1 to n.
a Work out 4!
b Explain why 10 must be a factor of 9!
c Explain why none of the numbers
10! + 2, 10! + 3, 10! + 4, 10! + 5, 10! + 6, 10! + 7
is a prime number.

2 Bertrand's Hypothesis states that there is at least one prime number between n and $2n$, for any integer $n > 1$. Use Bertrand's Hypothesis to show that the number of primes between 1 and 2^n is at least n.

3 The proper factors of a number n are the factors of n not including n itself.
a Write down all the proper factors of 8.
b Show that the sum of the proper factors of 10 is 8.
A number is called perfect if it is equal to the sum of its proper factors.
c Show that 6 is a perfect number.
d Show that 28 is a perfect number.
Let $n = 2^{p-1}(2^p - 1)$.
e Work out the value of n when $p = 2$ and when $p = 3$.
When p is a prime number and $2^p - 1$ is a prime number, $n = 2^{p-1}(2^p - 1)$ is a perfect number.
f Find one more perfect number.

Unit 2 | 4 Decimals and estimation

Key Points

- A recurring decimal is one where one or more figures in the number repeat.
- A fraction will convert to a terminating decimal if the only prime factors in its denominator are 2 and/or 5. Otherwise, the fraction will convert to a recurring decimal.
- All recurring decimals can be converted to fractions.
- When writing numbers correct to 1 significant figure round the first non-zero figure up if the second figure is 5 or more.
- When working out an estimate for the value of an expression, round each number correct to 1 significant figure.

You learnt to express a number as the product of its prime factors in section 1.1

A

Questions in this chapter are targeted at the grades indicated.

1   Convert each recurring decimal to a fraction. Give each fraction in its simplest form. Do **not** use a calculator.

   a $0.\dot{2}$

   b $0.\dot{8}\dot{3}$

   c $0.\dot{5}1\dot{3}$

   d $2.\dot{5}\dot{4}$

   e $0.\dot{1}254\dot{6}$

2   Convert each recurring decimal to a fraction. Give each fraction in its simplest form. Do **not** use a calculator.

   a $0.0\dot{7}$

   b $0.6\dot{7}\dot{5}$

   c $4.73\dot{2}$

   d $6.03\dot{4}\dot{5}$

   e $2.80\dot{9}1\dot{2}$

ResultsPlus
Examiners tip

For a think what single digit decimal, when squared, gives an answer that is approximately 0.1

3   Work out estimates for each of the following.

   a $\sqrt{0.1}$

   b $\sqrt{0.46}$

   c $\sqrt{0.046}$

4 $y = \dfrac{aT^4}{10^8}$ $T = 6182,\ a = 5.6704$

   Work out an estimate for the value of y.

5 $x = \dfrac{X - VT}{\sqrt{1 - V^2}}$

   $X = 6.4,\ V = 0.58,\ T = 2.91$

   Work out an estimate for the value of x.

6 A tank is partly filled with water. The surface of the water is a rectangle 19.8 cm long and 18.8 cm wide. 2.2 cm³ of oil is poured on the surface of the water and completely covers it. Work out an estimate for the thickness of the layer of oil. Give your answer in mm.

> **ResultsPlus**
> **Examiner's tip**
>
> The 2.2 cm³ of oil can be thought of as a rectangle with the same dimensions as the water and with unknown thickness.

7 $v^2 = u^2 + 2as$ $\qquad u = 0.89$ $\qquad\qquad a = -0.64$ $\qquad\qquad s = 0.48$

Work out an estimate of the value of v.

8 Use the result that $x^2 - y^2 = (x - y)(x + y)$ to work out an estimate for the value of $102.1^2 - 98.1^2$

9 Work out an estimate of the value of $\dfrac{103.5^2 - 97.5^2}{103.5^2 + 97.5^2}$

> **Challenge yourself**
>
> This is harder than anything you will encounter in the exam, but the underlying maths is covered in your GCSE course. Have a go and see how you do.
>
> **1** A rational number is a number that can be written as a fraction $\frac{a}{b}$ where a and b are integers and $b \neq 0$. All other numbers, for example $\sqrt{3}$, are called irrational numbers.
>
> Investigate whether the following numbers are rational or irrational.
>
> **a** $\frac{5}{9}$ $\qquad\qquad\qquad$ **b** 2.5
>
> **c** $\frac{1}{\sqrt{3}}$ $\qquad\qquad\quad$ **d** $0.4\dot{5}$
>
> **e** $\pi + 3$ $\qquad\qquad$ **f** $\sqrt{5}$
>
> **g** $\sqrt{45} - \sqrt{5}$ $\qquad$ **h** 0.042
>
> **i** $\frac{\sqrt{8} + \sqrt{2}}{\sqrt{2}}$ $\qquad\quad$ **j** 0.02222…
>
> **k** $\frac{1 - \sqrt{3}}{\sqrt{3}}$ $\qquad\quad$ **l** 0.0003
>
> **m** $\frac{20}{3}$ $\qquad\qquad\quad$ **n** 2π
>
> **o** $\sqrt{18} \times \sqrt{2}$
>
> **2** How far away is the Andromeda Galaxy?
> The speed of light is 299 792.458 kilometres per second.
> A star in the Andromeda Galaxy is 2.66 million light years away.
> A light year is the distance light travels in one year.
> Estimate how far away in kilometres is the Andromeda Galaxy.

Unit 2 | 5 Indices, standard form and surds

Key Points

- A number is in standard form when it is in the form $a \times 10^n$ where $1 \leqslant a < 10$ and n is an integer.
- For non-zero values of a
  $$a^0 = 1$$
- For any number n
  $$a^{-n} = \frac{1}{a^n}$$
- Indices can be fractions. In general,
  $$a^{\frac{1}{n}} = \sqrt[n]{a}$$
- In particular, this means that:
  $$a^{\frac{1}{2}} = \sqrt{a} \text{ and } a^{\frac{1}{3}} = \sqrt[3]{a}$$
- A number written exactly using square roots is called a surd.
- These two laws can be used to simplify surds.
  $$\sqrt{m} \times \sqrt{n} = \sqrt{mn} \qquad \frac{\sqrt{m}}{\sqrt{n}} = \sqrt{\frac{m}{n}}$$
- To rationalise the denominator of $\dfrac{a}{\sqrt{b}}$ you multiply the fraction by $\dfrac{\sqrt{b}}{\sqrt{b}}$.

A

Questions in this chapter are targeted at the grades indicated.

A⋆

1   Find the value of:

a 9^0 b 6^{-1} c 7^{-2} d $\left(\frac{1}{2}\right)^{-4}$ e $(-4)^{-3}$

f $\left(\frac{25}{81}\right)^{-\frac{1}{2}}$ g $\left(\frac{2}{3}\right)^0$ h $\left(2\frac{1}{4}\right)^{-\frac{1}{2}}$ i $\frac{1}{8^{-2}}$ j $\left(\frac{16}{81}\right)^{-\frac{1}{4}}$

2   Find the value of:

a $8^{\frac{2}{3}}$ b $32^{\frac{2}{5}}$ c $10\,000^{-\frac{3}{4}}$ d $\left(\frac{100}{9}\right)^{-\frac{3}{2}}$ e $\left(\frac{16}{81}\right)^{\frac{3}{2}}$

f $\left(\frac{64}{27}\right)^{-\frac{2}{3}}$ g $(32)^{-\frac{3}{5}}$ h $(0.0016)^{\frac{3}{4}}$ i $\left(\frac{125}{64}\right)^{-\frac{2}{3}}$ j $(2.25)^{-\frac{3}{2}}$

3   Simplify:

a $\sqrt{48}$ b $\sqrt{300}$ c $\sqrt{180}$ d $\sqrt{56}$

e $\dfrac{8 + \sqrt{40}}{2}$ f $\dfrac{15 - \sqrt{200}}{5}$ g $\dfrac{18 - \sqrt{72}}{3}$ h $\dfrac{24 + \sqrt{128}}{4}$

4   Write the following expressions in the form $k\sqrt{3}$ where k is an integer.

a $\sqrt{75}$ b $\sqrt{243} - \sqrt{48}$

c $\sqrt{108} + \sqrt{12} - \sqrt{27}$ d $\sqrt{300} + 2\sqrt{27} - 5\sqrt{75}$

5   Expand these expressions. Write your answers in the form $a + b\sqrt{c}$ where a, b and c are integers.

a $\sqrt{7}(5 + \sqrt{7})$ b $(1 + \sqrt{2})(3 + \sqrt{2})$ c $(5 - \sqrt{3})(\sqrt{3} + 1)$

d $(2\sqrt{5} - 3)(2\sqrt{5} + 7)$ e $(5 - \sqrt{2})^2$ f $(5 - \sqrt{2})^3$

6   Rationalise the denominators and simplify your answers.

a $\dfrac{6}{\sqrt{3}}$ b $\dfrac{8 - \sqrt{2}}{\sqrt{2}}$ c $\dfrac{15\sqrt{2}}{\sqrt{5}}$ d $\dfrac{28 + 3\sqrt{7}}{\sqrt{7}}$

7   A rectangle has a length of $(10 + \sqrt{2})$ cm and a width of $(3\sqrt{2} + 5)$ cm. Work out the perimeter and area of the rectangle. Give your answers in their simplest form.

8 A rectangle has an area of $(30 - 8\sqrt{3})$ cm². The length of one of the sides of the rectangle is $2\sqrt{3}$ cm. Find the length of the other side of the rectangle. Give your answer in the form $a + b\sqrt{c}$ where a, b and c are integers.

9 The lengths of the two shorter sides of a right-angled triangle are $\sqrt{7}$ cm and $2\sqrt{3}$ cm. Find the length of the hypotenuse.

10 a Rationalise the denominator of $\dfrac{1}{\sqrt{7}}$

   b Expand $(2 + \sqrt{7})(1 + \sqrt{7})$.
     Give your answer in the form $a + b\sqrt{7}$ where a and b are integers.

11 The value of a car can be modelled by the equation:

    $V = 17\,000 \times (0.9)^t$

   where V = the value of the car in £s and t = age from new in years.
   a Find V when $t = 0$.
   b Find V when $t = 4$.
   c Find the age of the car when the price first falls below £10 000.
   d Sketch a graph showing V against t.

> **Challenge yourself**

This is harder than anything you will encounter in the exam, but the underlying maths is covered in your GCSE course. Have a go and see how you do.

1 Work out:

   a $(\sqrt{3} + 1)(\sqrt{3} - 1)$ b $(6 + \sqrt{2})(6 - \sqrt{2})$

   c $(\sqrt{2} + \sqrt{5})(\sqrt{2} - \sqrt{5})$ d $(3\sqrt{7} + 1)(3\sqrt{7} - 1)$

2 What do you notice about all your answers in question 1 ?

3 Rationalise the denominator of these expressions.
   Simplify your answers as fully as possible.

   a $\dfrac{2}{\sqrt{3} + 1}$ b $\dfrac{12}{\sqrt{7} - 2}$ c $\dfrac{\sqrt{5}}{2 + \sqrt{5}}$ d $\dfrac{\sqrt{2} + 1}{3 - \sqrt{2}}$

   e $\dfrac{1 + \sqrt{2}}{5 - \sqrt{2}}$ f $\dfrac{2\sqrt{3} + \sqrt{2}}{\sqrt{3} - \sqrt{2}}$ g $\dfrac{1 - 5\sqrt{3}}{\sqrt{3} - 2}$ h $\dfrac{2\sqrt{7} + 1}{3 - \sqrt{7}}$

4 A rectangle has an area of $(31 - 8\sqrt{2})$ cm². The length of the rectangle is $(5 + \sqrt{2})$ cm. Work out the width of the rectangle. Give your answer in the form $a + b\sqrt{c}$ where a, b and c are integers.

5 Solve these equations, giving your answers in their simplest form ensuring that any fractions have whole number denominators.

   a $\sqrt{2}\,x + 5 = 2x + \sqrt{2}$ b $5x - \sqrt{3} = 7 - \sqrt{3}\,x$

   c $\dfrac{\sqrt{7}\,x}{2} - 1 = \dfrac{3}{4} + \sqrt{7}\,x$ d $\dfrac{1 - \sqrt{3}\,x}{6} = x + \dfrac{\sqrt{3}}{2}$

   e $\dfrac{1}{\sqrt{3}\,x + 2} = \dfrac{4}{\sqrt{3} - x}$ f $\dfrac{\sqrt{2} + x}{\sqrt{2}(1 - x)} = \sqrt{8} + 1$

Unit 2 | 6 Expressions and sequences

Key Points

○ The index laws can be used to simplify expressions

$x^m \times x^n = x^{m+n}$

$x^m \div x^n = x^{m-n}$

$(x^m)^n = x^{mn}$

Also

$x^0 = 1$

$x^{-m} = \frac{1}{x^m}$

$x^{\frac{1}{n}} = \sqrt[n]{x}$

A

Questions in this chapter are targeted at the grades indicated.

1 Simplify fully:

a $6x^3y^{-2} \times 2x^{-4}y^4$

b $(x^{-5})^3$

c $(20x^6y) \div (4x^{-2}y^5)$

d $(x^{-3})^0$

e $(27x^{12}y^3)^{\frac{1}{3}}$

f $(-2x^{\frac{1}{2}}y^{\frac{1}{3}})^6$

g $\dfrac{18x^5\,y^{-2}}{9x^{-3}\,y^2}$

h $\sqrt{(36x^8y^{-3})}$

2 Write in the form x^n:

a $\dfrac{1}{\sqrt{x}}$

b $\dfrac{1}{x^5}$

c $\left(\dfrac{1}{\sqrt[3]{x}}\right)^2$

d $\sqrt[4]{x^5}$

3 Write in the form kx^n:

a $\left(\dfrac{4}{\sqrt{x}}\right)^3$

b $\dfrac{7}{\sqrt[3]{x^2}}$

c $\left(\dfrac{5}{\sqrt[4]{x}}\right)^2$

d $\dfrac{10}{4\sqrt{x^5}}$

4 In each of the following, find the value of k.

a $x^k \times x^7 = (x^{-4})^2$

b $\dfrac{1}{x^4} = x^2 \times x^k$

c $(x^2)^k = \dfrac{x^4}{\sqrt{x}}$

d $\dfrac{1}{\sqrt[3]{x}} = \dfrac{\sqrt{x}}{x^k}$

A☆

5 Given that $y = 2^p$, write in terms of y:

a 2^{p+1}

b 2^{-p}

c 2^{p-3}

d 4^p

e $\dfrac{1}{8^p}$

⟩ **Challenge yourself**

This is harder than anything you will encounter in the exam, but the underlying maths is covered in your GCSE course. Have a go and see how you do.

A quadratic sequence is one where the nth term is of the form $an^2 + bn + c$.

1   Write down the first five terms for each of the following sequences.
   a $n^2 + n + 2$
   b $n^2 + 4n + 1$
   c $2n^2 + n + 3$
   d $n^2 - 3n + 5$
   e $6 - n^2$
   f $10 - n - 3n^2$

2   a Copy and complete the grid for the first 5 terms of the sequence $an^2 + bn + c$.

	$n = 1$		$n = 2$		$n = 3$	$n = 4$	$n = 5$
Sequence	$a + b + c$		$4a + 2b + c$		$9a + 3b + c$		
First difference		$3a + b$		$5a + b$			
Second difference			$2a$				

   b What do you notice about all the terms in the first difference row?
   c What do you notice about all the terms in the second difference row?

3   a Copy and complete the grid for this sequence 6, 12, 20, 30, 42…

Sequence	6		12		20	30	42
First difference		6		8			
Second difference			2				

   b By comparing the second differences in **Q3a** with the second differences in **Q2a**, write down the value of a for the sequence 6, 12, 20, 30, 42…
   c By comparing the first differences in **Q3a** with the first differences in **Q2a**, write down the value of b for the sequence 6, 12, 20, 30, 42…
   d By comparing the terms of the sequence in **Q3a** with the terms of the sequence in **Q2a**, write down the value of c for the sequence 6, 12, 20, 30, 42…
   e Hence, write down an expression, in terms of n, for the nth term of the sequence 6, 12, 20, 30, 42…

4   Find an expression, in terms of n, for the nth term of the following sequences.
   a 7, 11, 17, 25, 35…
   b −1, −1, 1, 5, 11…
   c 0, 7, 18, 33, 52…
   d 5, 6, 5, 2, −3…
   e −1, 7, 17, 29, 43…
   f −6, −25, −54, −93, −142

Unit 2 | 7 Expanding brackets and factorising

Key Points

- An expression where the terms have common factors can be factorised using one bracket.
- To multiply out two brackets, multiply each term in the first bracket by each term in the second bracket.
- Quadratic expressions of the form $x^2 + bx + c$ can be factorised by finding two numbers whose product is $+c$ and whose sum is $+b$.
- Any expression that can be written in the form of the difference of two squares can be factorised using the result
  $a^2 - b^2 = (a + b)(a - b)$
- Quadratic expressions of the form $ax^2 + bx + c$ can be factorised using factorising by grouping.

A

Questions in this chapter are targeted at the grades indicated.

1 Factorise completely and give your answer in its simplest form.
  a $24a^4b^3 + 18a^2b$
  b $4(x + 5) + (x + 5)^2$
  c $(x - 7)^2 - 3(x - 7)^3$
  d $4d(c + 2d) + 6(c + 2d)^2$
  e $5x(x + 3)^3 - 4(x + 3)^4$
  f $(x - 4)(x + 1) - (x - 4)^2$

2 Factorise completely and give your answer in its simplest form.
  a $ax + ay + bx + by$
  b $mx - ny - nx + my$
  c $3a + ab + 3b + b^2$
  d $x^3 - x^2 + x - 1$
  e $p^4 + p^3 + 5p + 5$
  f $8cd - 2c - 4d + 1$

3 Expand and simplify:
  a $(x + 1)(x - 3)(x + 2)$
  b $(x + 2)^3$
  c $(x - 1)^3$
  d $(2x + 5)(x - 3)(x - 1)$

4 Factorise:
  a $x^2 - 7x + 10$ b $x^2 + 5x - 24$ c $x^2 + 12x + 36$
  d $x^2 - 7x - 60$ e $3x^2 + x - 4$ f $5x^2 - 9x - 2$
  g $7x^2 - 31x + 12$ h $5x^2 + 2x - 3$ i $5x^2 + 8x + 3$
  j $8x^2 - 14x - 15$ k $6x^2 - 19x - 7$ l $4x^2 - 17x - 15$
  m $4x^2 + 8x - 21$ n $6x^2 - 43x + 7$ o $4x^2 - 4x - 35$
  p $6x^2 + 11x + 4$ q $6 - 5x - 4x^2$ r $5 + 8x - 4x^2$
  s $21 - x - 2x^2$ t $7x + 6 - 3x^2$

5 Factorise   a $x^2 - 16$ b $m^2 - n^2$ c $25 - a^2$ d $4y^2 - 1$

6 Factorise $4p^2 - 9q^2$

7 Factorise completely   a $8p^2 - 2$ b $9x^2y - 4y$ c $4y^2 - 4$ d $4y^3 - y$

8 Express $(x + 1)^2 - (y + 1)^2$ as a product of 2 factors.

9 Here is a number pattern that describes the number of counters in a square pattern.

1 counter	1st pattern	$1^2 = 0^2 + 1$
2×2 counters	2nd pattern	$2^2 = 1^2 + 2 + 1$
3×3 counters	3rd pattern	$3^2 = 2^2 + 3 + 2$
4×4 counters	4th pattern	$4^2 = 3^2 + 4 + 3$

   a Complete the following:

     10th pattern $10^2 = \underline{\quad} + \underline{\quad} + \underline{\quad}$

     nth pattern $n^2 = \underline{\quad} + \underline{\quad} + \underline{\quad}$

   b Show that the right hand side of the nth pattern simplifies to n^2.

10 Factorise:

   a $4x^2 - 1$ b $9a^2 - 16b^2$

   c $25 - 36d^2$ d $x^4 - y^2$

   e $32x^3 - 8xy^2$ f $a^6 - 4a^6b^2$

   g $(2x + 1)^2 - (2x - 1)^2$ h $(3x + 1)^2 - (2x - 3)^2$

   i $(4x - 5)^2 - (3x + 2)^2$

11 Work out the following without using a calculator.

   a $48^2 - 46^2$

   b $1.1^2 - 0.9^2$

   c $37.5^2 - 12.5^2$

   d $205^2 - 195^2$

12 Factorise fully and give your answer in its simplest form.

   a $x(2x + 1)^3 - 6(2x + 1)^2$

   b $3x(x - 4)^2 + (x - 4)(x + 6)$

   c $(x - 1)^4 - (3x - 5)(x - 1)^2$

> **Challenge yourself**

This is harder than anything you will encounter in the exam, but the underlying maths is covered in your GCSE course. Have a go and see how you do.

a Expand and simplify $(x + y)^3$

b Expand and simplify $(x + y)^4$

c Expand and simplify $(x + y)^5$

d Copy the grid below and use your answers to **a**, **b** and **c** to complete the last three rows. In each row the terms should go in descending powers of x.

$(x + y)^0 =$ 　　　　　　　　　　　　　 1

$(x + y)^1 =$ 　　　　　　　　 x 　　　　 $+ y$

$(x + y)^2 =$ 　　　　　 x^2 　　 $+ 2x$ 　　 $+ y^2$

$(x + y)^3 =$ 　　 x^3 　 $+ 3x^2y$ 　　 $+$

$(x + y)^4 =$

$(x + y)^5 =$

e Rewrite the grid from part **d** but this time just use the coefficient of each term.

f Describe how each row in the triangle of numbers in part **e** can be produced from the row above. This triangle is called Pascal's Triangle. There are many patterns that can be found and explored within the triangle.

g Continue the pattern to complete the next three rows of Pascal's Triangle.

h Use Pascal's Triangle to write out the expansion for $(x + y)^9$

i Use the numbers in Pascal's Triangle to help you expand and simplify the expressions:
  i $(x + 1)^8$
  ii $(2a + 1)^5$
  iii $(a - b)^7$
  iv $(2a - b)^6$
  v $(3a + 2b)^4$

Unit 2 | 8 Algebraic fractions and algebraic proof

Key Points

○ To simplify algebraic fractions, first factorise the numerator and denominator if possible and then divide the numerator and denominator by any common factors.

○ To add or subtract algebraic fractions, find a common denominator and then add or subtract the numerators, just as you would for numerical fractions.

○ To multiply algebraic fractions, multiply the numerators and multiply the denominators.

○ To divide algebraic fractions, multiply the first fraction by the reciprocal of the second fraction (turn the second fraction upside down).

○ Algebraic expressions should always be given in their simplest form.

○ Algebra can be used to prove statements.

> *You learnt to factorise quadratic expressions in Section 8.4.*

---

1 Simplify fully:

a $\dfrac{2(x-2)}{x^2-5x+6}$

b $\dfrac{3x+6}{x^2-2x-8}$

c $\dfrac{x^2+4x-5}{x^2+7x+10}$

d $\dfrac{4x^2-12x}{x^2-9x+18}$

> *Questions in this chapter are targeted at the grades indicated.*

> A*

2 Simplify fully:

a $\dfrac{2}{x}+\dfrac{1}{x+3}$

b $\dfrac{3}{x+1}\times\dfrac{x}{x-2}$

c $\dfrac{6}{x}\div\dfrac{x-5}{2x}$

d $\dfrac{4}{x+5}-\dfrac{1}{x-2}$

e $\dfrac{2x-6}{x+4}\div\dfrac{x-3}{x}$

f $\dfrac{4}{2x-1}+\dfrac{1}{x+1}$

g $\dfrac{3}{x-1}-\dfrac{2}{2x+4}$

h $\dfrac{3}{x+5}\times\dfrac{5x+25}{12x+6}$

3 Simplify fully:

a $\dfrac{x^2-9}{x^2-7x-30}$

b $\dfrac{2y^2-10y-12}{3y^3-3y}$

c $\dfrac{12p^2+11p-5}{4p^2-11p-20}$

d $\dfrac{4a^2-b^2}{2a^2-5ab-3b^2}$

4 Simplify fully:

a $\dfrac{5}{2x}+\dfrac{3}{2x^2+8x}$

b $\dfrac{x^2-3x-4}{x^2-4}\times\dfrac{x^2+3x-10}{x^2+6x+5}$

c $\dfrac{2}{6x-15}-\dfrac{1}{4x^2-25}$

d $\dfrac{2x^2+x-3}{5x^2-3x}\div\dfrac{x^2-1}{5x^2+2x-3}$

e $3-\dfrac{2}{x+3}-\dfrac{12}{x^2-9}$

f $\dfrac{3}{x^2+4x-21}+\dfrac{1}{x^2-7x+12}$

A03

5 Prove that the sum of the squares of any two consecutive integers is always an odd number.

A03

6 Karen says she can prove that the sum of an odd number and an even number is always odd. She says that $2 + 3 = 5$ and as 5 is an odd number this proves that an odd number added to an even number is an odd number. This isn't a proof. Explain why.

A03

7 Prove that $(5n + 1)^2 - (5n - 1)^2$ is a multiple of 4 for all positive integer values of n.

A03

8 Prove that the difference between the squares of any two consecutive odd numbers is always an even number.

A03

9 Prove that $(2n + 3)^2 - (2n - 3)^2$ is always a multiple of 6.

A03

10 Prove that the difference between the cubes of any two consecutive odd numbers is always an even number.

A03

11 Prove that $(an + b)^2 - (an - b)^2$, where a and b are positive integers, is a multiple of 4 for all positive integer values of n.

Challenge yourself

This is harder than anything you will encounter in the exam, but the underlying maths is covered in your GCSE course. Have a go and see how you do.

1 A farmer has 600 m of fencing. He is going to use the fencing to make a rectangular sheep pen. One side of the sheep pen will be along an existing straight hedge.
Let x represent the length of the shorter side of the rectangle.

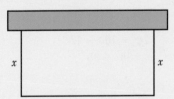

a Write down an expression, in terms of x for the longer side of the rectangle.
b Write down an equation for the area, A, of the sheep pen.

2 A ball is thrown in the air. After t seconds its height, h metres above the ground, is given by the equation
$h = 10t - 1 - 5t^2$
Find the maximum height above the ground reached by the ball.

Unit 2 | 9 Angles, polygons and circles

Key Points

○ The sum of the internal angles of a polygon with n sides is $180 (n − 2)°$

○ The sum of the external angles of a polygon with n sides is $360°$.

○ A tessellation of a flat surface by a repeating pattern of polygons is a covering of the surface without gaps or overlaps.

○ The tangents to a circle from an exterior point are equal in length.

Questions in this chapter are targeted at the grades indicated.

1 Prove that the sum of the interior angles of an n-sided polygon is $180(n − 2)°$.

A03   **A**

2 ABCDE is a regular pentagon. The lines BE and AC meet at the point X. Work out the size of angle CXD.

A02

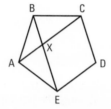

3 ABCDEFGH is a regular octagon. Work out the size of angle HBG.

A02

4 A, B, C, D and E are five points equally spaced around a circle, centre O. M is the midpoint of AB and N is the midpoint of AE. Work out the size of angle MON.

A02

5 ABCDE is a pentagon with interior angles a, b, c, d and e in order of size around the pentagon. The differences between a and b and between b and c and between c and d and between d and e are all the same. Find the size of angle c.

A03   **A***

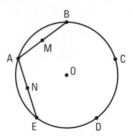

*6 **a** Prove that the only regular polygons which can tessellate a flat plane are the equilateral triangle, the square and the regular hexagon.

A03

A 2-regular tessellation consists of a tessellation using two different regular polygons.

b Show that a tessellation involving squares and octagons is a 2-regular tessellation.

c Find two other possible 2-regular tessellations.

* **7** ABE and ACF are tangents at B and C, respectively, to the circle, centre O.

D is a point on the circle such that CD is parallel to ABE.

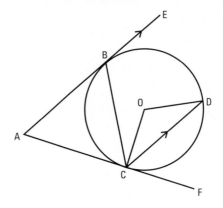

Prove that angle COD = 2 × angle CAB.

Challenge yourself

Penrose tilings

Penrose tiles can be used to give a non-repeating covering of a flat surface. Just as tessellations have importance in the study of crystalline structures, so do Penrose tilings in the study of quasicrystals.

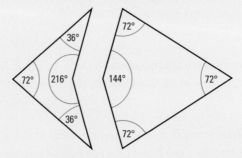

The two Penrose tiles shown above can be used to make irregular tessellations.

Show that there are seven different ways of fitting Penrose tiles around a point without overlap or gaps. One has been shown for you.

Unit 2 | 10 Area and volume

Key Points

○ Circumference and area of a circle.

$C = 2\pi r = \pi d$

$A = \pi r^2$

Area of sector $= \dfrac{x}{360} \times \pi r^2$

Arc length $= \dfrac{x}{360} \times 2\pi r$

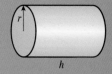

○ Volume of a prism, cylinder, pyramid and cone.

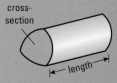

cross-section

length

$V =$ area cross-section $\times$ length

$V = 2\pi r^2 h$

$V = \frac{1}{3} \times$ base area $\times$ height

$V = \frac{1}{3} \times \pi r^2 h$

---

1 For this shape, calculate:

   a the perimeter

   b the area.

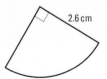

2.6 cm

Questions in this chapter are targeted at the grades indicated.

A02
A03

A

2 The diameter of the Japanese 5 Yen coin is 22 mm.
The diameter of the hole is 5 mm.
The coin is 3 mm thick.

   a A cube of metal of side 10 cm was used to make some of
these coins.
How many coins were made from 1 cube of metal?

   b One reason for the hole was to save metal.
How much metal was saved?

   c Sometimes square holes were used.
What size hole would give a coin of the same volume?

A02
A03

3 Find the missing volume or length.

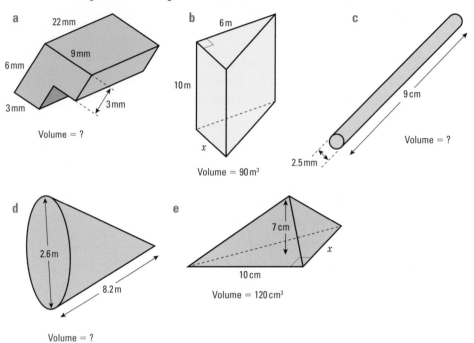

a
22 mm
9 mm
6 mm
3 mm
3 mm
Volume = ?

b
6 m
10 m
x
Volume = 90 m³

c
9 cm
2.5 mm
Volume = ?

d
2.6 m
8.2 m
Volume = ?

e
7 cm
10 cm
x
Volume = 120 cm³

4 The area of each Frisbee is shown.
Calculate the value of x.

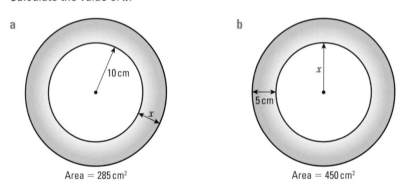

a
10 cm
x
Area = 285 cm²

b
x
5 cm
Area = 450 cm²

5 This interlocking building brick is made from a hollow cuboid with a uniform thickness of 2 mm. It has six round solid studs 2 mm high arranged in rows 3 mm apart. Bricks fit tightly on top of each other.

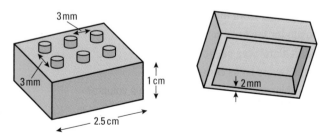

3 mm
3 mm
1 cm
2.5 cm
2 mm

a Calculate the volume of plastic used to make a brick.
Similar bricks can be made using this table of dimensions.

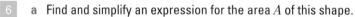

Stud height	$2x$
Distance between rows of studs	$3x$
Thickness of plastic	$2x$
Height of exterior cuboid	$10x$

b Find and simplify a formula for the volume V of plastic used to make a brick.

c Calculate the value of x when the volume V is 5 cm³.

6 a Find and simplify an expression for the area A of this shape.

b Plot the graph of A against x.

c Use your graph to find the value of x when $A = 24$

d i Use algebra to find the value of x when $A = 30$

   ii Check your answer using the graph.

A*
A02
A03

7 The cylinder and cube have the same volume. Find and simplify an expression for the radius r in terms of x.

A02
A03

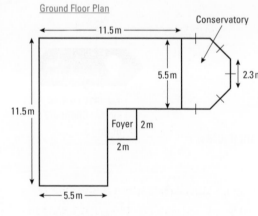

8 The diagram shows the plan and elevations of a house.

A

Ground Floor Plan   First Floor Plan

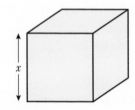

Conservatory

Aerial Plan of Roof   Front Elevation

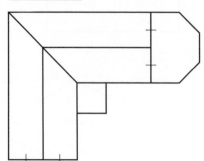
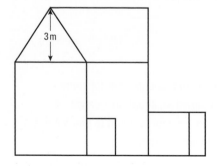

Sketch the house and show the dimensions.

9   The heights of the ground floor and first floor are both 2.4 m.
    The height of the Foyer is 2.2 m. The height of the Conservatory is 2.6 m. Calculate:
    a   the area of each floor
    b   the total exterior perimeter of each floor
    c   the volume of air in each floor
    d   the volume of air in the loft space.

10   Draw floor plans, elevations and sketches of a simple building in your school or neighbourhood (you may need to estimate some of the dimensions or use a laser measure). Repeat the above calculations.

> **Challenge yourself**

1   The area of each shape is given.

    a
    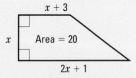

    b
    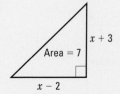

    c

    i   Write down an equation involving x.
    ii   Solve the equation to find x, correct to 3 significant figures.

    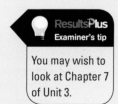

    ResultsPlus
    Examiner's tip

    You may wish to look at Chapter 7 of Unit 3.

2   The area of this shape is 48 units.
    a   Write down two equations involving x and y.
    b   Find x and y.

    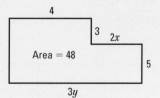

3   The volume of this cuboid is 100 units.
    a   Write down an equation involving x.
    b   Use trial an improvement to find x correct to 2 decimal places.

    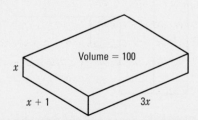

Unit 3 | 11 Number (2)

Key Points

○ **Standard form** is used to represent very large (or very small) numbers.

A number is in standard form when it is in the form $a \times 10^n$ where $1 \leqslant a < 10$ and n is an integer.

○ When entering numbers in standard form on a scientific calculator use the $\boxed{\text{EXP}}$ key or $\boxed{\times 10^x}$ key

Answers in standard form when read from the calculator display MUST be written in the form

$a \times 10^n$ where $1 \leqslant a < 10$

Questions in this chapter are targeted at the grades indicated.

A

1 $T = \dfrac{t}{\sqrt{1 - \dfrac{v^2}{c^2}}}$

$t = 2.8 \times 10^{-6}, v = 2.1 \times 10^8, c = 3 \times 10^8$

a Work out the value of T.

v is increased by 20%.

b Calculate the percentage change in the value of T.

2 $v^2 = \dfrac{2as}{p + 2q}$

$a = 64, s = 4.8 \times 10^7, p = 2.5 \times 10^{-4}, q = 8 \times 10^{-6}$

Calculate the value of v.

3 A room is 4 m long, 6 m wide and 3 m high. The number of air molecules in 1 cm³ is 2.6×10^{19}

Work out the number of air molecules in the room.

4 A car emits 119 g of carbon dioxide for each mile it is driven.

There are 5.4 million cars in a country. On average, each car is driven 12 000 miles in a year. Work out the total mass of carbon dioxide emitted by these cars in one year.

5 The intensity, I, in suitable units, of the radiation emitted by an object with a temperature $T\,°C$ is given by the rule

$I = kT^4$

$\quad = 5.7 \times 10^{-8} \times T^4$

a A star has a temperature of $3 \times 10^5\,°C$. Work out the intensity of the radiation emitted.

The intensity, expressed in the same units, from another star is 5×10^{12}.

b Calculate the temperature of this star.

A

6 The energy requirement of the UK is currently 310 gigawatts.

A commercial wind turbine can generate 1.27 megawatts.

The energy demand in the UK is expected to increase by 12% in the next 10 years. How many commercial wind generators would be need to provide this energy demand?

$1\,Gw = 10^9$ watts, $1\,Mw = 10^6$ watts

7 A googol is written as 1 followed by 100 zeroes. Write the number 200 googols in standard form.

A★

AO3

8 The Earth is approximately a sphere of radius 6.4×10^6 metres .

The inner core of the Earth is approximately a sphere with a radius that is 20% of the radius of the Earth.

The outer core of the Earth reaches from the edge of the inner core to the mantle. The thickness of the outer core is 2300 km.

The inner core is made of solid iron. $1\,cm^3$ of this iron has a mass of 12.5 grams.

The outer core is made of liquid iron. $1\,cm^3$ of this iron has a mass of 10.2 grams.

Work out the ratio of the mass of the inner core to the mass of the outer core.

(You will need the formula: volume of a sphere of radius $r = \frac{4}{3}\pi r^3$)

AO3

9 Which is bigger, 2^{1000} or 10^{302}?
You must explain your answer.

AO3

10 A sequence starts $\frac{1}{10}$ $\frac{1}{100}$ $\frac{1}{10000}$ where each term is the square of the preceding term.
Which term is the first term to be below 10^{-500}?

⚙ **Challenge yourself**

The Large Hadron Collider

The Large Hadron Collider (LHC) is a huge tube bent into the shape of a circle. Small particles (protons) travel around at huge speeds and smash into each other to produce smaller particles.

The radius of the LHC is 4.3 km.

The speed of light is 3×10^8 metres per second.

a Work out how long it takes light to travel once around the LHC.

Einstein's special theory of relativity predicts that the mass M kg, of an object when travelling with speed v metres per second is related to its mass m kg when at rest by

$$M = \frac{m}{\sqrt{1 - \frac{v^2}{c^2}}}$$

c is the speed of light.

The rest mass of a proton is 1.67×10^{-27} .

b Work out the mass of a proton travelling at a speed which is 99% of the speed of light.

Unit 3 | 12 Upper and lower bounds

Key Points

- The **upper bound** of a number is the highest value which rounds down to that number.
- The **lower bound** of a number is the lowest value which rounds up to that number.

  Let $S = x + y$.

  Then upper bound of S = the upper bound of x + upper bound of y.

  Let $D = x - y$.

  Then upper bound of D = upper bound of x + lower bound of y.

  Let $P = xy$.

  Then upper bound of P = upper bound of x × upper bound of y.

  Let $Q = \dfrac{x}{y}$.

  Then upper bound of Q = upper bound of x ÷ lower bound of y.

- For the lower bounds of S and P, use the lower bounds of x and y.
- The lower bound of D = lower bound of x − upper bound of y.
- The lower bound of Q = lower bound of x ÷ upper bound of y.

---

1 The diagram shows a solid prism. The cross-section of the prism is a trapezium of height 10.1 cm. The lengths of the parallel sides of the trapezium are 4.5 cm and 7.8 cm. The length of the prism is 16.0 cm.

Questions in this chapter are targeted at the grades indicated.

A03 A

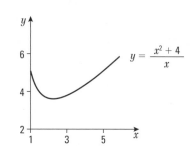

Diagram NOT drawn accurately

All the measurements are given correct to the nearest mm.

The solid prism is made from metal. Exactly 1 cm³ of metal has a mass of 6.4 g correct to 1 decimal place.

Work out the upper bound for the total mass of the prism. Give your answer correct to 3 sig. fig.

2 Here is a graph of $y = \dfrac{x^2 + 4}{x}$

Given that $y = \dfrac{a^2 + 4}{a}$

where $a = 4.5$ correct to 1 decimal place,

calculate the upper bound of y.

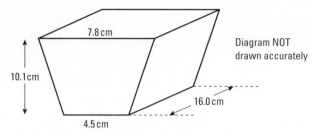

A

A02
A03

3 The diagram shows a field with length 48 m correct to the nearest m and width 36 m correct to the nearest m. A path, exactly 1 m wide goes all the way around the inside of the field.

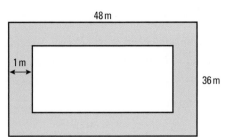

Calculate the upper bound and the lower bound of the area of the path.

4 The area of a square is 630 m^2 correct to the nearest 10 m^2. Calculate the lower bound for the perimeter of the square.

A02

5 $T = \frac{1}{2}mv^2$ $m = 400$ (2 sig. fig.), $v = 3.2 \times 10^3$ (2 sig. fig). Halima says that the value of T could be 2×10^9. Could Halima be correct?

6 A formula for describing the growth of a population with time is

$P = S\left(1 + \dfrac{r}{100}\right)^n$ where r % is the growth rate per year, S is the starting population and n is the number of whole years since the start.

For one population, S is exactly 10000, but $r = 5$ correct to the nearest whole number.

Use the formula to find the difference between the upper and the lower bounds of the population after exactly 10 years. Give your answer correct to 3 significant figures.

7 Write down: i the upper bound and   ii the lower bound of these numbers.
a 3.4 (1 decimal place)   b 2.0 (1 decimal place)
c 24.8 (1 decimal place)

8 Write down: i the upper bound and   ii the lower bound of these numbers.
a 4.36 (2 decimal places)   b 5.08 (2 decimal places)
c 34.66 (2 decimal places)

9 Write down: i the upper bound and   ii the lower bound of these numbers.
a 48 (2 significant figures)   b 560 (2 significant figures)
c 0.0065 (2 significant figures)

10 Write down: i the upper bound and   ii the lower bound of these numbers.
a 456 (3 significant figures)   b 5600 (3 significant figures)
c 0.00577 (3 significant figures)

11 Write down the upper bounds of these numbers.
a 7.4 (1 decimal place)   b 8.0 (1 decimal place)
c 6.43 (2 decimal places)   d 460 (2 decimal places)
e 3450 (3 significant figures)

12 Write down the lower bounds of these numbers.
   a 8.3 (1 decimal place)   b 10.0 (1 decimal place)
   c 8.00 (2 decimal places)   d 45 (2 significant figures)
   e 4000 (3 significant figures)

13 $x = 4.0$ (1 d.p.), $y = 5.2$ (1 d.p.) Work out the lower bounds of
   a $x + y$ b xy

14 $m = 3.5$ (1 d.p.), $n = 5.7$ (1 d.p.) Work out the upper bounds of
   a $m + n$ b mn

15 $a = 3.44$ (2 d.p.), $b = 1.85$ (2 d.p.) Work out the lower bounds of
   a $a + b$ b ab c a^2

16 The diagram shows a circle with a second concentric circle taken out. The diameter
   of the circle is 10.8 cm. The width of the shaded region is 2.5 cm. All measurements are
   correct to the nearest mm.

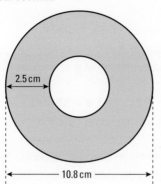

2.5 cm

Diagram NOT
drawn accurately

10.8 cm

Calculate the lower bound and the upper bound of the area of the shaded region.
Use $\pi = 3.14159$

17 The length of a rectangle is L metres and the width of the rectangle is W metres. Each
   measurement is correct to the nearest cm. Find, in terms of L and W the difference
   between the lower bound and the upper bound of the area of the rectangle.

18 The percentage error in a measurement is
   $$\frac{\text{upper bound} - \text{quoted measurement}}{\text{quoted measurement}} \times 100$$
   The length of a rod is quoted to be 125 cm correct to the nearest cm.
   a Show that the percentage error is 0.4%
   A rectangle is 125 cm by 100 cm, with each measurement correct to the nearest cm.
   b Calculate the maximum percentage error in the calculated area of the rectangle.

* **19** $y = 0.5at^2$, $a = 4.5$ (1 d.p.), $t = 6.8$ (1 d.p.)
   a Find the lower bound of y.
   b Find the upper bound of y.

* **20** $p = \dfrac{l^2}{w}$, $l = 6.44$ (2 d.p.) and $w = 5.45$ (2 d.p.)

    a   Calculate the lower bound of p.

    b   Calculate the upper bound of p.

    c   Write p correct to an appropriate number of significant figures.

* **21** $s = ut + \frac{1}{2}at^2$, $u = 4.0$ (1 d.p.), $t = 4.8$ (1 d.p.), $a = 5.5$ (1 d.p.)

    Calculate the difference between the lower bound and the upper bound of s.

* **22** $w = \dfrac{x^2 - y^2}{2z}$, $x = 52$, $y = 26$, $z = 10$

    a   Work out the exact value of w.

    b   If instead x, y and z have been written correct to 2 sig. figs, work out the value of the upper bound and the value of the lower bound.

    c   Calculate the percentage difference between the exact value of w and the upper bound of w.

* **23** $y = a\cos x°$, $a = 4.2$ (1 d.p.) and $x = 60°$ (2 s.f.)

    Show that the lower bound of y is 2.04 (3 s.f.) and find the upper bound of y.

* **24**   **a**   Expand $(a + b)^2$.

    $y = n^2$ n is written correct to the nearest whole number.

    b   Show that the upper bound of y is $n^2 + n + \frac{1}{4}$

    c   Find a similar expression for the lower bound of y.

* **25** $v^2 = u^2 + 2as$ $s = 28$ (2 s.f.), $a = 9.8$ (1 d.p.), $u = 48$ (2 s.f.)

    Work out the lower bound of v. Work out the upper bound of v.

* **26**   The edge of a cube is 10 cm correct to the nearest cm. Work out the difference between the upper bound and the lower bound of the volume of the cube.

* **27**   Jim was at the racing track. He estimated that the length of the track he could see was 100 m correct to the nearest 10 metres. He timed a car as taking 5 seconds to the nearest second along the track he could see.

    Work out the lower bound and the upper bound for the average speed of the car.

    Give your answers correct to 1 decimal place.

* **28**   The acceleration a, metres per second, of a falling object due to gravity can be found by using the formula $a = \dfrac{2h}{t^2}$, where h metres is the height fallen and t seconds is the time taken.

    A ball takes 0.8 seconds (correct to 1 decimal place) to fall a distance 2.55 m, correct to the nearest centimetre.

    Calculate the upper bound of a. Give your answer correct to 1 d.p.

* **29** $h = \dfrac{v^2}{2g}$, $v = 45$ (2 significant figures), $g = 9.8$ (1 decimal place). Work out the difference between the upper bound of h and the lower bound of h.

* **30** $p = 63$ correct to 2 significant figures, $q = 3.2$ correct to 2 significant figures.

    Find the value of $\dfrac{p}{q}$ to an appropriate accuracy.

* 31 $y = \dfrac{k}{x^2}$, $k = 4.84$ (2 decimal places), $x = 2.40$ (2 decimal places)

   a Work out the upper bound of y.

   b Work out the lower bound of y.

   c Write down the value of y correct to an appropriate number of significant figures.

* 32 The area of a square is 230 cm² correct to 2 significant figures. Work out the least possible perimeter of the square.

* 33 A cuboid has edges of length 4.2 cm, 6.8 cm and 10.0 cm, all measured correct to the nearest mm.

   The mass of the cuboid is 1.6 kg correct to one decimal place.

   Calculate the lower bound of the density of the cuboid. Give your answer in grams per cm³ correct to 3 significant figures.

* 34 The length, L m, of a tyre skid when a car suddenly brakes from a speed s metres per second is given by $L = \dfrac{s^2}{2d}$ where d metres per second squared is the deceleration.

   L was measured to be 15.6 correct to 1 decimal place and d was 7 correct to the nearest whole number.

   Calculate the lower bound of s. Give your answer correct to 1 d.p.

Challenge yourself

Binary stars and exoplanets

The closest star system to the Sun is a pair of stars, a binary (double star) system called Alpha Centauri A and B.

The formula $\dfrac{1}{M} = \dfrac{1}{m_A} + \dfrac{1}{m_B}$ is used by astronomers to work out the mass m_B of one of the stars,

if M and m_A can be measured.

For the Alpha Centauri system

$m_A = 2.2 \times 10^{30}$ kg and $M = 7.2 \times 10^{29}$ kg,

both correct to 2 significant figures.

a Find the upper bound and the lower bound of m_B.

Astronomers can also use techniques to discover planets outside our solar system.

For this system $m_A = 2 \times 10^{30}$ kg and $M = 5 \times 10^{27}$ kg, both correct to 1 significant figure.

Find the lower bound and the upper bound of m_B, the mass of the planet.

Unit 3 | 13 Linear equations

Key Points

You learnt
how to expand
brackets
in Unit 2
Sections 8.1
and 8.3

You learnt
to find the
LCM of two
numbers
in Unit 2
Section 1.2

○ In any equation, the value of the left-hand side is always equal to the value of the right-hand side. So whatever operation is applied to the left-hand side must also be applied to the right-hand side.

○ When solving an algebraic equation which includes fractions, eliminate all fractions by multiplying each term by the LCM of the denominators.

○ Problems can sometimes be solved by setting up equations to represent statements given in the problem.

○ When setting up an equation, define all unknowns used that have not already been defined.

○ Units must be consistent on both sides of an equation.

A

Questions in this chapter are targeted at the grades indicated.

1 Solve:

a $\frac{3}{4}(2x + 3) - 3\frac{1}{2} = \frac{4}{5}(1 - x)$

b $\frac{4}{3} - \frac{5}{7}(6 - x) = \frac{2}{3}(3 + 2x)$

2 Solve:

a $\frac{(x + 4)}{(x - 7)} = \frac{(x - 6)}{(x - 1)}$

b $\frac{(2x - 5)}{(2x + 3)} = \frac{(x - 7)}{(x + 8)}$

A03

3 Jasmin buys some pens costing 35p each and some pencils costing 20p each. She buys 35 items altogether and spends a total of £9.70. How many pens and how many pencils does Jasmin buy?

A03

4 A man drives to work, a total of 45 kilometres, he drives at 40 km/h when he is in moving traffic and at 75 km/h for the rest of the time. The journey takes him 50 minutes. Work out for how long he drove in moving traffic.

A03

5 Jim has 60 coins worth a total of £4.60. Some of the coins are 10p pieces and some are 5p pieces.
Work out how many 10p pieces Jim has.

A
AO2
AO3

6

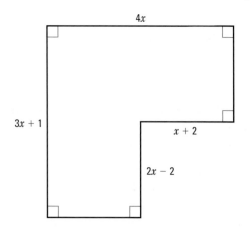

4x

3x + 1

x + 2

2x − 2

Diagram **NOT** accurately drawn

All the measurements are in centimetres.
The area of this shape is 100 cm².
Work out the length of the shortest side of the shape.

> **Challenge yourself**

This is harder than anything you will encounter in the exam, but the underlying maths is covered in your GCSE course. Have a go and see how you do.

a Here is an identity
($\equiv$ means identity)
$ax(x + 1) + bx + c \equiv 3x^2 + 5x + 2$
Write down the coefficient of x^2 on the left-hand side of the identity.
Write down the coefficient of x^2 on the right hand side of the identity.
As this is an identity, then there must be an equal number of each power of x on each side. Hence, work out the value of a. (This process is known as equating the coefficients of x^2)
Equate the coefficients of x to work out the value of b.
Equate the constant terms to work out the value of c.

b Work out the values of a, b and c in each of the following
  i $4x^2 + 5x - 3 \equiv ax(x + 1) + bx + c$
  ii $ax(x - 1) + bx + c \equiv 1 + 6x - 2x^2$
  iii $2x^2 + 1 \equiv ax^2 + b(x + 2) + c$
  iv $x^2 + x + 1 \equiv ax(x + 2) + b(x + 1) + c$
  v $4 - 3x^2 \equiv ax(x - 3) + b(x - 2) + c$
  vi $x^2 + 2x \equiv ax(x + 5) + b(x - c)$
  vii $4x^2 + x - 10 \equiv ax(x - 1) + b(x - c)$
  viii $x^2 + 6x + 2 \equiv a(x + b)^2 + c$
  ix $3x^2 + 2x - 1 \equiv a(x + b)^2 + c$
  x $6 - 3x - x^2 \equiv a(x + b)^2 + c$

ResultsPlus
Examiner's tip

Remember that there are two terms in x on the left-hand side of the identity.

Unit 3 | 14 Inequalities and formulae

> ### 🔧 Key Points
>
> - You solve a linear inequality using a method similar to that used to solve a linear equation.
> - If you multiply or divide an inequality by a negative number then you must reverse the inequality sign.
> - You can show the points that satisfy an inequality on a graph.
> - Lines which are boundaries for regions that *do* include values on the line are shown as solid lines. Lines which are boundaries for regions that do *not* include values on the line are shown as dotted lines.
> - You use a graphical method to solve several linear inequalities in two variables and find the solution set.
> - To change the subject of a formula, you isolate the terms of the new subject.
> - When the new subject occurs more than once, isolate all terms and then factorise.

You learnt to solve linear equations in Chapter 4 of unit 3

You learnt to draw straight-line graphs in Chapter 9 of unit 2

A

Questions in this chapter are targeted at the grades indicated.

1 Solve these inequalities.

a $\dfrac{3x}{2} - 2(1 - 2x) \geqslant \dfrac{16x + 7}{2}$

b $\dfrac{1 - 4x}{6} + 2 \leqslant \dfrac{2x + 5}{4}$

c $\dfrac{3(2x - 1)}{4} < \dfrac{7}{10} - \dfrac{2(3 - 5x)}{5}$

2 Find all the possible integer values of x in each of these inequalities.

a $0 \leqslant \dfrac{x - 1}{4} \leqslant 1$

b $-3 < \dfrac{4x - 1}{2} \leqslant 4$

c $-5 \leqslant 3 - 2x < 2$

d $-9 \leqslant \dfrac{2(1 - 2x)}{3} \leqslant 1\tfrac{1}{3}$

3 Find the least integer which satisfies the inequality

$\dfrac{x}{4} - \dfrac{2x - 3}{6} > \dfrac{5 - 3x}{2}$

4 Find the greatest integer which satisfies the inequality

$\dfrac{5 - 2x}{3} \leqslant 7 - 3x + \dfrac{1}{6}.$

5 Find all the possible integer values of x that satisfy $x^2 < 4$.

6 Find all the possible integer values of x that satisfy $5x^2 - 80 < 0$.

A03

A03

7 Each diagram shows a region bounded by some lines. In each case
   i Write down the equations of each of the lines.
   ii Write down the inequalities satisfied by the coordinates of the points in the unshaded region.
   iii If x and y are integers, write down the coordinates of the points in each unshaded region.

a
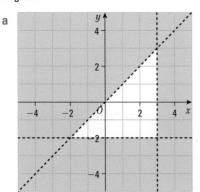

b
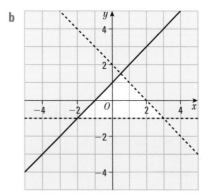

8
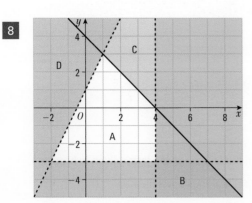

Use inequalities to describe the regions:
   a A   **b** B   **c** C   **d** D.

9 **a** Draw a diagram to show the region which satisfies all these inequalities:
     $2x + 3y < 6$ $x < 4$ $x > 0$ $y > -1$
   b Mark, with a cross, all the points with integer coordinates which satisfy all the inequalities.

10 Draw a diagram to show the region which satisfies all these inequalities:
   $y \leqslant 2x + 3$ $x + y \leqslant 3$ $y \geqslant -2$

11 Draw a diagram to show the region which satisfies all these inequalities:
   $x + y \leqslant 4$ $y \leqslant x + 4$ $4y - x \geqslant 1$

12 **a** Draw a diagram to show the region which satisfies all these inequalities:
     $5x + 2y < 10,$ $y > -2,$ $y < x + 2$
   b Mark, with a cross, all the points with integer coordinates which satisfy all the inequalities.

13 In each of the following formulae, change the subject to the letter given in brackets.

a $s = ut + \frac{1}{2}at^2$ [a]

b $V = \frac{4}{3}\pi r^3$ [r]

c $A = 2\pi rh + 2\pi r^2$ [h]

d $V = \pi r^2(h_1 - h_2)$ [r]

e $V = \pi r^2(h_1 - h_2)$ [h_1]

f $A = \frac{1}{2}(a + b)h$ [b]

14 In each of the following formulae, change the subject to the letter given in brackets.

a $3a + 2b = ab + 5$ [a]

b $B = \sqrt[3]{a - 2}$ [a]

c $y = \sqrt{\dfrac{2x + 1}{x}}$ [x]

d $5(p - 2) = 2q(p + 1)$ [p]

e $m = \dfrac{xy}{x + y}$ [x]

f $k = \sqrt[w]{5 - v^2}$ [v]

15 In each of the following formulae, change the subject to the letter given in brackets.

a $t = \dfrac{3c + 5}{1 - c}$ [c]

b $k = \sqrt{\dfrac{a(5 - b)}{4 - d}}$ [d]

c $y = \dfrac{2(A - 3b)}{A - 1}$ [b]

d $m = n + p\sqrt{t}$ [t]

e $\dfrac{1}{f} = \dfrac{1}{u} - \dfrac{1}{v}$ [v]

f $y = \dfrac{1 + x^2}{1 - x^2}$ [x]

16 Find all the possible integer values of x which satisfy this inequality.

$$\frac{1 - 2x}{3} \leqslant 5x - 4 < 8 - \frac{x}{2}$$

17 Explain clearly why there are no values of x that satisfy the inequality $x^2 < -5$

Challenge yourself

This is harder than anything you will encounter in the exam, but the underlying maths is covered in your GCSE course. Have a go and see how you do.

Linear Programming can be used to find the possible solutions to a problem where there are a number of constraints. The constraints are written down as inequalities and these are then used to find a graphical solution to the original problem.

1 The organisers of a barbeque need to buy some sausages and burgers. They are going to buy x packets of sausages and y packets of burgers.
  a Sausages come in packs of 6 and burgers come in packs of 8. The organisers need to ensure that they have at least 120 sausages and burgers altogether. Use this information to write down an inequality and show that $3x + 4y \geqslant 60$.
  b Sausages and burgers both cost £2 per packet. The organisers have a maximum of £50 to spend. Use this information to write down an inequality and show that $x + y \leqslant 25$.
  c Some people coming to the barbeque don't eat sausages so the organisers must buy at least 4 packets of burgers. Use this information to write down an inequality.
  d Explain why $x \geqslant 0$ should also be included as an inequality.
  e Draw a diagram to show the region that satisfies all four inequalities.
  f If the organisers decide to buy as many sausages as possible, write down the number of packets of sausages and the number of packets of burgers that they should buy.

2 A company makes two different types of tables.
  Each week the company makes x round tables and y rectangular tables.
  a Round tables take 30 hours each to make and rectangular tables take 15 hours each to make. Each week, the company has a total of 300 hours to make tables. Use this information to show that $2x + y \leqslant 10$.
  b The company has to make at least two circular tables and at least two rectangular tables per week. Write down two inequalities to express this information.
  c Draw a diagram to show the region that satisfies all three inequalities.
  d Using your diagram, write down all the possible solutions to the problem.
  e Round tables sell for a profit of £550 and rectangular tables sell for a profit of £400. Assuming that the company will sell all the tables that they make, how many of each table should the company make each week in order to maximise their profit?

3 James wants to buy some cakes to take into the office to celebrate his birthday.
  Doughnuts cost 25p each and iced buns cost 20p each. He doesn't want to spend more than £3.
  He must buy at least 5 iced buns. James needs to buy at least 12 cakes in total.
  James buys x doughnuts and y iced buns.
  a Use the information given in the problem to write down 3 inequalities in x and y.
  b Draw a diagram to show the region that satisfies all three inequalities.
  c James decides to buy as many doughnuts as possible and spends all his money. Write down the number of doughnuts and the number of iced buns that he buys.

4 An organic fruit and vegetable company sells fruit boxes. It sells large and small boxes of fruit. One day it has a total of 300 apples. Each small fruit box contains 6 apples and each large fruit box contains 10 apples. The company know that they will be able to sell at least 30 boxes and they have 20 customers that must have a small box of fruit, the rest of the customers will accept large or small boxes. The company makes up x small boxes and y large boxes of fruit.

    a Use the information given in the problem to write down 3 inequalities in x and y.

    b Draw a diagram to show the region that satisfies all three inequalities.

    c The company wants to make up as many large boxes of fruit as possible. How many large boxes and how many small boxes of fruit should they make?

5 A theatre advertises a 'Summer Special'. The adult ticket price is £40 and each child pays £20. There are 1200 seats in the theatre. In order to break even, the theatre must make at least £32 000 from ticket sales. The theatre sells x adult and y child tickets.

    a Use the information given in the problem to write down two inequalities in x and y.

    b Draw a diagram to show the region that satisfies all three inequalities.

    c Write down the greatest number of adults that could attend the performance. Calculate the total amount of money that the theatre will make from ticket sales for this number of adults and children.

    d Write down the greatest number of children that could attend the performance. Calculate the total amount of money that the theatre will make from ticket sales for this number of children and adults.

Challenge yourself

This is harder than anything you will encounter in the exam, but the underlying maths is covered in your GCSE course. Have a go and see how you do.

It is sometimes useful to combine two formulae.

1 The volume of a cylinder is given by the formula $V = \pi r^2 h$. The surface area of the cylinder is given by the formula $A = 2\pi r(r + h)$. Given that the volume of a cylinder is 200π cm^3, find an expression for the surface area of the cylinder in terms of r.

2 A cuboid is of length x cm, width y cm and height y cm. Given that the surface area of the cuboid is 60 cm^2, write down a formula for the volume of the cuboid in terms of y.

3 Given that $s = \frac{1}{2}(u + v)t$ and $v = u + at$

    a find an expression for v in terms of u, a and s.

    b find an expression for s in terms of v, u and a.

Unit 3 | 15 More graphs and equations

Key Points

○ The graph of a quadratic function is called a parabola. All parabolas have a line of symmetry. The equation of a parabola is $y = ax^2 + bx + c$.

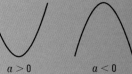

$a > 0$ $a < 0$

You can use graphs to help solve associated equations.

○ You solve quadratic equations of the form $ax^2 + bx + c = 0$ by reading off the x-coordinate where $y = ax^2 + bx + c$ crosses the x-axis.

○ You solve quadratic equations of the form $ax^2 + bx + c = mx + k$ by reading off the x-coordinate at the point of intersection(s) of $y = ax^2 + bx + c$ with the straight-line graph $y = mx + k$.

○ All cubic functions can be written in the form $y = ax^3 + bx^2 + cx + d$

○ Reciprocal functions have the equation $y = \dfrac{k}{x}$

○ The x- and y-axes are called asymptotes; the graph never crosses or touches these lines.

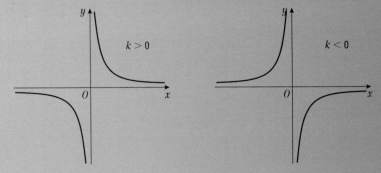

○ Exponential functions have the equation $y = a^x$ and $y = a^{-x}$.
The x-axis is an asymptote for these equations.

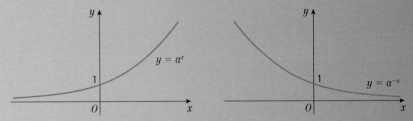

○ A trial and improvement method can be used to find approximate solutions to equations which cannot be solved exactly.

A

Questions in this chapter are targeted at the grades indicated.

1 Draw the graph for each of the following equations.

a $y = \frac{4}{x}$ for values of x from -10 to $+10$

b $y = 4^x$ for values of x from -5 to $+2$

c $y = x(1 - x)(x + 2)$ for values of x from -3 to $+2$

2 Sketch the graph for each of the following giving the coordinates of the points of intersection with the x and y axes.

a $y = (x + 5)(x - 2)$ b $y = x(2 - x)$

c $y = (6 - x)(2x - 1)$ d $y = x(x + 4)(x - 2)$

e $y = x^2(3 - x)$ f $y = (2 - x)(x + 3)(x - 1)$

3 Here are six graphs.

a
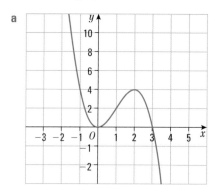

b
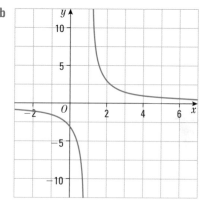

c
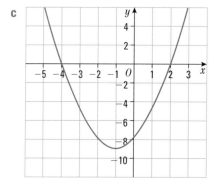

d
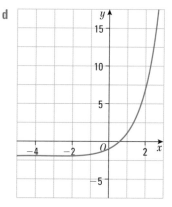

e
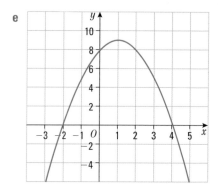

f
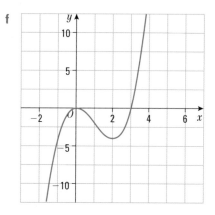

Here are six equations.

Match each equation to one of the graphs.

Give reasons for your answers.

 i $y = -x^2 + 2x + 8$ ii $y = 3^x - 2$ iii $y = x^3 - 3x^2$

 iv $y = x^2 + 2x - 8$ v $y = 3x^2 - x^3$ vi $y = \dfrac{3}{x - 1}$

4 The graph with equation $y = ax^3 + 3x^2 - 7$ goes through the point
(2, 37).
Work out the value of a.

5 The diagram shows the graph of
$y = 2x^2 - 7x + 4$

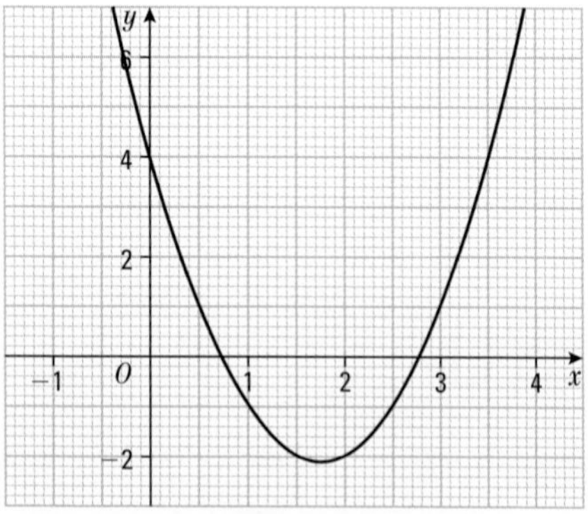

 a Use the graph to find estimates of
the solutions to the equations:

  i $2x^2 - 7x + 4 = 0$

  ii $2x^2 - 7x + 4 = 3$

  iii $2x^2 - 7x + 4 = -0.5$

 b By drawing suitable straight lines on this
graph it is possible to solve the following
equations. In each case, write down the
equation of the straight line.

  i $2x^2 - 7x + 4 = 0$ ii $2x^2 - 5x + 1 = 0$ iii $2x^2 - 8x + 5 = 0$

6 a Draw the graph of $y = 2x^2 + 3x - 1$ for values of x from -3 to $+2$.

 b By drawing suitable straight lines on your graph, find estimates for the solutions of
the equations:

  i $2x^2 + x - 1 = 0$

  ii $2x^2 + 4x + 2 = 0$

  iii $2x^2 - x - 2 = 0$

7 Find the coordinates of the points of intersection of the parabolas
$y = 2x(x - 3)$ and $y = x^2 - 3x - 2$.

8 a Draw the graph of $y = x^3 - x^2 - 5x - 2$ for values of x from -3 to $+4$.

 b Use your graph to help explain why:

  i the equation $x^3 - x^2 - 5x - 6 = 0$ has only one solution.

  ii the equation $x^3 - x^2 - 5x + 3 = 0$ has three solutions.

 c How many solutions will the equation $x^3 - x^2 - 5x - 1 = 0$ have?
Give a reason for your answer.

 d By drawing suitable straight lines or parabolas on this graph it is possible to solve
the following equations. In each case, write down the equation of the straight line or
parabola.

  i $x^3 - x^2 - 7x - 1 = 0$

  ii $x^3 - 5x - 4 = 0$

  iii $x^3 - 2x^2 - 4x = 0$

 e By drawing a suitable parabola on your graph, find estimates for the solutions of the
equation $x^3 - 2x^2 - 5x + 2 = 0$.

A*

9   Jack wants to solve the equation $2^x = x^2 + 2x$
     Explain how Jack could use a graphical method to find estimates of the solution of this
     equation.
     a   Find estimates for the solutions of $2^x = x^2 + 2x$
     b   Use trial and improvement to find solutions of the equation $2^x - x^2 - 2x = 0$ correct
         to 2 decimal places.

10   The points with coordinates (1, 6) and (3, 24) lie on the graph with equation $y = pq^x$
     where $q > 0$.
     a   Draw a sketch of the graph $y = pq^x$
     b   Find the value of p and the value of q.
     c   The point with coordinates (5, k) lies on the curve.
         Find the value of k.

Challenge yourself

This is harder than anything you will encounter in the exam, but the underlying maths is covered in your
GCSE course. Have a go and see how you do.

A combination of algebra and graph drawing can be used to solve problems involving
maximum and minimum problems.

A company wants to make some small boxes. They will use sheets of card that measure
15 cm by 21 cm. Each box will be made by cutting a square from each corner of the piece
of card. The company want the boxes to have the largest possible volume.

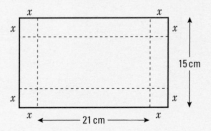
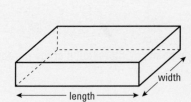

a   Write down expressions for the length and width of the box.
b   Write down an equation in terms of x for the volume, V, of the box.
c   Draw the graph of your equation in part b.
d   Use your graph to find as accurately as possible:
    i   the value of x that gives the largest possible volume
    ii the largest possible volume for the box.
e   The company decides that they want their boxes to have a volume of exactly 300 cm³. Use your graph
    from part c to find an approximate value for x. Using trial and improvement, find a value for x correct to
    2 decimal places so that the box has a volume of 300 cm³.

Unit 3 | 16 Quadratic and simultaneous equations

Key Points

- A quadratic equation can always be written in the form $ax^2 + bx + c = 0$ where $a \neq 0$, b and c represent numbers. A quadratic equation always has two solutions (or roots) although these solutions may be equal.
- All quadratic equations can be written in the form $p(x + q)^2 + r = 0$
- The process of writing a quadratic equation in this form is done using a process called completing the square.
- Some quadratic equations can be solved by factorising.
- All quadratic equations that have a solution can be solved either by completing the square or by using the quadratic formula.
- The quadratic formula used to solve $ax^2 + bx + c = 0$ is

$$x = \frac{-b \pm \sqrt{b^2 - 4ac}}{2a}$$

The solutions of a quadratic equation link into the drawing of its graph as the solutions give the x-coordinates of the points of intersection of the graph with the x-axis, see Unit 3 Chapter 6.

- A pair of simultaneous equations where both are linear can be solved by either an algebraic or graphical method.

You learnt to solve linear equations in Chapter 4 of unit 3

- The solution of a pair of simultaneous equations where both are linear represents the point of intersection between two straight lines.
- A pair of simultaneous equations where one is linear and one is quadratic can be solved by either an algebraic or graphical method.

You learnt to draw straight line graphs in Chapter 9 of unit 2

- The solution of a pair of simultaneous equations where one is linear and one is quadratic represents the points of intersection of a straight line and a quadratic curve.
- The equation of a circle with centre (0, 0) and radius r can be written $x^2 + y^2 = r^2$
- A pair of simultaneous equations where one is linear and one is the equation of a circle can be solved by either an algebraic or graphical method.

You learnt to draw graphs of quadratic curves in Chapter 6 of unit 3

1   Solve these equations. Where necessary give your solutions correct to 3 significant figures.

a $x^2 + 6x = 0$
b $7x^2 + 28x = 0$
c $x^2 + 7x - 30 = 0$
d $x^2 + 6x + 3 = 0$
e $x^2 - 5x - 36 = 0$
f $x^2 + 5x + 2 = 0$
g $x^2 - 49 = 0$
h $3x^2 - 5x - 1 = 0$
i $2x^2 - x - 6 = 0$
j $x^2 + 8x + 16 = 0$
k $6x^2 - 11x + 3 = 0$
l $3x^2 + 8x + 3 = 0$

Questions in this chapter are targeted at the grades indicated.

A

ResultsPlus
Examiner's tip

Try factorising as a method of solution then, if necessary, use the quadratic formula.

A

ResultsPlus
Examiners tip

Let the width of the rectangle be x, so the length is $(x + 10)$.

2 The length of a rectangle is 10 cm more than its width. The area of the rectangle is 56 cm². Find the width of the rectangle.

3 The difference between two numbers is 2. The sum of their squares is 650. Find the two numbers.

4 Find the length of each side of this right-angled triangle.
The measurements are all given in cm.

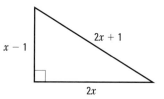

5 Solve these simultaneous equations.

ResultsPlus
Examiners tip

When an equation involves fractions, first get rid of fractions by multiplying by the LCM of the denominators of the fractions.

a $3x + 2y = 5$
   $5x - 3y = 21$

b $7a - 3b = -13$
   $4a + 5b = 6$

c $4p - 2q - 13 = 0$
   $5p - 6q = 18$

d $3a = 4b - 26$
   $2a = 31 - 7b$

e $y - 3x = 9$
   $4y + 5x = 2$

f $3a - 8b = 4$
   $9a + 4b = 5$

g $\dfrac{x}{3} + \dfrac{y}{2} = 3$
   $\dfrac{5x}{2} - 3y = -45$

h $\dfrac{2x}{5} - \dfrac{4y}{3} = 3$
   $8y - x = -11$

i $\dfrac{x - 1}{4} + \dfrac{y + 2}{3} = 0$
   $\dfrac{1 - 2x}{3} - \dfrac{y - 4}{4} = 5$

A03

6 Show that the simultaneous equations $3y - 2x = 4$ and $4x - 6y + 18 = 0$ have no solutions.

A02
A03

7 The cost of 3 adult and 2 child tickets for a museum is £31.50. The cost of 5 adult and 3 child tickets for the same museum is £51.25. Work out the cost of one child and one adult ticket.

A02
A03

8 The cost of 2 kg of apples and 5 kg of bananas is £6.25. The cost of 7 kg of apples and 3 kg of bananas is £11. Work out the cost of 1 kg of apples and 1 kg of bananas.

A03

9 Mr Brown bought 3 ice creams and 2 lollies. He paid £3.80.
Jenny bought 2 ice creams and 4 lollies. She paid £4.40.
If the ice creams cost x pence each and the lollies cost y pence each, work out the value of x and the value of y.

10 Rehana has 15 coins in her purse. Some of the coins are 2p coins and the rest are 5p coins. The total value of the coins in Rehana's purse is 54p. Find the number of 2p coins and the number of 5p coins.

A☆

ResultsPlus
Examiners tip

First rearrange each equation into a quadratic equation.

11 Solve these equations. Where necessary give your solutions correct to 3 significant figures.

a $x(3x + 5) = x + 5$

b $(4x - 7)(x + 1) = -1$

c $2x - 13 = 6x^2 - 10(x + 1)$

d $\dfrac{3}{x - 2} + \dfrac{8}{x + 3} = 2$

e $\dfrac{x - 1}{x - 2} + \dfrac{x + 11}{x + 3} = 4$

f $\dfrac{1}{x} + \dfrac{2}{x + 1} = \dfrac{4}{x - 1}$

12 a Use the quadratic formula to attempt to solve these equations.

      i $x^2 - 3x + 7 = 0$ ii $3x^2 + 7x + 5 = 0$

  b Explain why you were unable to solve either of the equations in part **a**.

  c Hence, write down a rule that you can use to work out whether or not a quadratic equation can be solved.

13 Determine which of these equations have solutions.

  If an equation can be solved then give the roots in simplified surd form.

  a $x^2 + 3x - 7 = 0$ b $x^2 + 3x + 7 = 0$ c $9x^2 - 12x + 4 = 0$

  d $5x^2 + 8x - 2 = 0$ e $2x^2 + 6x - 5 = 0$ f $4x^2 - 28x + 49 = 0$

  g $3x^2 + 8x + 10 = 0$ h $4x^2 + 21x - 18 = 0$

14 The smallest of three positive consecutive numbers is n. Three times the square of the middle number is 34 more than the sum of the squares of the other two numbers. Find n.

15 A train travels 160 km. If the train was travelling 16 km/h slower, the journey would take 30 minutes longer. Find the average speed of the train.

16 Rob spends £9.20 on buying some pencils. If the pencils had been 3p cheaper, he could have bought 6 more.

  How many pencils did he buy?

17 When a javelin (or any other object) is thrown, its height above the point of projection can be calculated.

  This is done using the formula $y = Vt\sin a - 5t^2$

  where y is the height of the javelin at time t seconds after it has been thrown

  V is the velocity (speed) with which the object was thrown

  a is the angle to the horizontal at which the object was thrown

  t is the time elapsed since the object was thrown.

  a A javelin is thrown at 30° to the horizontal with a velocity of 24 ms^{-1}.

    Work out the height of the javelin after:

    i 1 second   ii 2 seconds.

  b A javelin is thrown at 30° to the horizontal with a velocity of 30 ms^{-1}.

    i Find the times at which the javelin was at a height of 10 m.

    ii For how long was the javelin more than 5 m above ground level?

      Give your answer correct to 1 decimal place.

  c A ball is thrown with a velocity of 10 ms^{-1} at an angle of 30° above the horizontal.

    It hits the ground at a point which is 2 m below the point of projection. Calculate the length of time that the ball is in the air.

18 The perimeter of a rectangle is 23 cm and its area is 30 cm^2. Work out the length and width of the rectangle.

19 The sum of the ages of a father and his son is 71 years. Seven years ago, the father was $8\frac{1}{2}$ times as old as his son. How old is the son now?

20 Solve these simultaneous equations.

a $y = 3x$
$y = x^2 - 10$

b $y - x = 7$
$y = x^2 + 6x + 13$

c $y = 2x^2 - 5x$
$2x - y = 3$

d $y = 3x^2 + 2x$
$y + 6x = 16$

e $x^2 + xy = 30$
$x - y = 17$

f $x^2 - 6 = xy$
$2x + y = 7$

21 Find the coordinates of the points of intersection of each circle and straight line.

a $x^2 + y^2 = 29$
$y = x + 3$

b $x^2 + y^2 = 17$
$y = 1 - x$

c $x^2 + y^2 = 2$
$y = 2x - 1$

d $x^2 + y^2 = 7$
$y = 2 + x$

22 a Solve the simultaneous equations

$x^2 + y^2 = 20 \qquad 2y = x + 10$

b What does your answer to part **a** tell you about the relationship between the circle $x^2 + y^2 = 20$ and the line $2y = x + 10$?

23 a Solve the simultaneous equations

$x^2 + y^2 = 6 \qquad 2y = 6 - x$

b What does your answer to part **a** tell you about the relationship between the circle $x^2 + y^2 = 6$ and the line $2y = 6 - x$?

24 A straight line can

i intersect a circle twice

ii touch the circle (be a tangent to the circle)

iii not intersect a circle.

For each of the following circles and straight lines determine which one of the above applies. If the line intersects or touches the circle then find these coordinates.

a $x^2 + y^2 = 10$
$y = 2 - x$

b $x^2 + y^2 = 2$
$y = x + 4$

c $x^2 + y^2 = 80$
$y = 2x$

d $x^2 + y^2 = 45$
$y + 2x = 15$

* 25 Four knives and six forks cost £13.60.
Six knives and five forks cost £16.40.
Work out the cost of a knife and the cost of a fork.

* 26 Solve the equation $\dfrac{x}{2x - 3} + \dfrac{4}{x + 1} = 1$

* 27 Draw suitable graphs to find estimates of the solutions of the simultaneous equations $x^2 + y^2 = 20$ and $x + y = 3$.

⟳ **Challenge yourself**

This is harder than anything you will encounter in the exam, but the underlying maths is covered in your GCSE course. Have a go and see how you do.

An athletics club is designing a running track that is in the shape of a rectangle with a semicircle at either end.

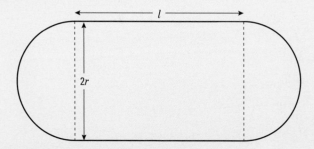

a   Write down an equation for the perimeter, P, of the running track.

b   Write down an equation for the area, A, of the rectangular region.

The perimeter of the track must be 500 m and the rectangular region must be 9600 m².

c   Show that $\pi r^2 - 250r + 4800 = 0$

d   Work out the possible values for the length of the rectangle and the radius of the semicircle.

e   Work out the maximum possible value of the area inside the track.

ResultsPlus
Examiner's tip

Use your equation for the area and draw a graph.

⟳ **Challenge yourself**

This is harder than anything you will encounter in the exam, but the underlying maths is covered in your GCSE course. Have a go and see how you do.

Simultaneous equations in three unknowns

1   a   Rearrange $2x + y = 5$ to make y the subject.

   b   Hence, write the equations $3x + 4y + z = 9$ and $x - 2y + z = -1$ in terms of x and z only.

   c   Solve the simultaneous equations
   $2x + y = 5$
   $3x + 4y + z = 9$
   $x - 2y + z = -1$

2   a   Eliminate b from the equations $4a + b - 2c = 7$ and $3a - b + c = 19$

   b   Eliminate b from the equations $4a + b - 2c = 7$ and $2a + 3b + 3c = -1$

   c   Hence, solve the simultaneous equations
   $4a + b - 2c = 7$
   $3a - b + c = 19$
   $2a + 3b + 3c = -1$

3 Solve each of the following sets of simultaneous equations.

a $3a + b + 2c = 15$
$5a - 3c = 3$
$4a + 2b - c = 4$

b $x + y + z = 1$
$3x - 2y - z = -3$
$7x - 5y = 3$

c $3a - 2b + 2c = 10$
$4a + b - c = 6$
$2a - 3b + 3c = 10$

d $2x + 5y - z = -10$
$x - y + 2z = 9$
$2x + 2y - z = 2$

e $3g + 2h + 6j = 8$
$2g - 3h + 4j = 14$
$5g - h + 2j = 10$

f $x + y + 2z = 4$
$3x - 2y + 5z = 13$
$4x + 3y - 3z = -27$

Circles

This work is beyond the GCSE specification although all the techniques involved are within the GCSE specification. This work demonstrates the links between some of the work already covered in algebra and coordinate geometry.

The general equation of a circle is $(x - a)^2 + (y - b)^2 = r^2$ where the centre of the circle is (a, b) and the radius r.

4 Write down the centre and radius of the circle of equation:

a $(x - 5)^2 + (y - 2)^2 = 100$
b $(x - 1)^2 + (y - 3)^2 = 49$
c $(x + 2)^2 + (y - 7)^2 = 64$
d $(x - 1)^2 + (y + 6)^2 = 16$
e $x^2 + (y - 4)^2 = 40$
f $(x + \frac{9}{2})^2 + (y - \frac{1}{4})^2 = 5$

5 Write down the equations of the circles with these given centres and radii.

a Centre $(3, 7)$, radius 8
b Centre $(1, 5)$, radius 3
c Centre $(-2, 3)$, radius 4
d Centre $(-2, -4)$, radius 10
e Centre $(\frac{1}{2}, -3)$, radius $\sqrt{12}$
f Centre $(-2, 0)$, radius $\sqrt{35}$

6   a Complete the square for $x^2 - 4x$
    b Complete the square for $y^2 - 8y$

You learnt how to complete the square in Section 7.5.

    c Hence, write down the equation
       $x^2 - 4x + y^2 - 8y - 5 = 0$ in the form $(x - a)^2 + (y - b)^2 = r^2$
    d Using your answer to part c write down the centre and radius of the circle
       represented by $x^2 - 4x + y^2 - 8y - 5 = 0$
    e Work out the centre and radius of the circle represented by:
       i $x^2 - 6x + y^2 - 10y - 15 = 0$ ii $x^2 + 2x + y^2 - 14y = 50$
       iii $x^2 + 10x + y^2 - 5y - \frac{1}{4} = 0$ iv $x^2 - 3x + y^2 + y = \frac{3}{2}$
       v $x^2 + y^2 + 5y - 2\frac{3}{4} = 0$ vi $x^2 - 6x + y^2 - 10y - 15 = 0$
       vii $2x^2 + 4x + 2y^2 - 12y = 6$ viii $4x^2 - 12x + 4y^2 + 16y = 24$

7   Find the length of the radius of the circle that passes through the point
    $(-1, 2)$ and has centre $(4, 7)$.

8   Find the length of the diameter of the circle that passes through the point
    $(-7, -1)$ and has centre $(-3, 1)$.

9   Find the equation of the circle that passes through the point $(5, 0)$ and
    has centre $(9, -3)$.

ResultsPlus
Examiner's tip

Pythagoras' Theorem can be used to find the length of a line joining two points.

10 The point $(1, -1)$ is on the circumference of the circle $x^2 + 4x + y^2 - 6y = 12$.
    a Work out the gradient of the line joining $(1, -1)$ and the centre of the circle.
    b Hence:
       i Work out the gradient of the tangent to the circle at the point $(1, -1)$
       ii Work out the equation of the tangent to the circle at the point $(1, -1)$

You learnt how to find the gradient in Chapter 9, unit 2.

You learnt about the connection between the gradients of perpendicular lines in Chapter 9, unit 2.

11 Work out the equation of the tangent at the point $(3, 1)$ on the circle $x^2 - 4x + y^2 + 10y = 8$.

12 Work out the equation of the tangent at the point $(2, 1)$ on the circle $(x + 4)^2 + (y - 1)^2 = 36$.

13 Work out the equation of the tangent at the point $(-2, 3)$ on the circle $x^2 - 6x + y^2 - 10y = -5$.

14 Find the coordinates of the points of intersection of the circles
    $x^2 + y^2 = 25$
    $x^2 - 12x + y^2 + 11 = 0$

Unit 3 | 17 Proportion

Key Points

You learnt how to set up equations in Section 4.5 →

- When two quantities are in direct proportion, this can be written as

  $y \propto x$ or $y = kx$

  where k is the constant of proportionality.

- When two quantities are in inverse proportion, this can be written as

  $y \propto \dfrac{1}{x}$ or $y = \dfrac{k}{x}$

  where k is the constant of proportionality.

A

Questions in this chapter are targeted at the grades indicated.

1 a x is directly proportional to the square of m.
Given that
$x = 108$ when $m = 6$,
express x in terms of m.
  b Work out the value of x when $m = 8$.
  c Work out the value of m when $x = 18.75$.

2 a g is directly proportional to the square root of t.
Given that
$g = 3$ when $t = 16$,
express g in terms of t.
  b Work out the value of g when $t = 100$.
  c Work out the value of t when $g = 15$.

3 The extension, e cm, of a stretched string is directly proportional to the tension, T newtons, in the string.
Given that
$e = 2.5$ when $T = 60$,
calculate the tension in the same string when the extension is 4 cm.

4 The energy, E joules, of a moving ball is directly proportional to the square of the speed, v m/s, of the ball.
When $E = 96$, $v = 8$.
Find the value of v when $E = 8.64$.

5 T is directly proportional to b. $T = 5.25$ when $b = 1.5$.
  a Show that $T = 3.5b$.
  b Work out the value of T when $b = 2.8$.

6 H is inversely proportional to the square of v so that $H = \dfrac{k}{v^2}$.
$H = 2.75$ when $v = 4$.
  a Work out the value of k.
  b Work out the value of H when $v = 5$.
  c Work out the value of v when $H = 9$.

7 The Body Mass Index (BMI) formula was first used by the Belgian statistician, Adolphe Quetelet (1796–1874). It is an internationally used measure which estimates a person's healthy weight depending on their height.

A person's BMI is directly proportional to their weight w (in kg) and inversely proportional to the square of their height h (in metres), i.e. BMI $= k \times \dfrac{w}{h^2}$, where k is a constant.

It is suggested that for most people $k = 1$, so that BMI $= \dfrac{w}{h^2}$.

	BMI
Underweight	Under 18.5
Normal	18.5 to 24.9
Overweight	25 to 29.9
Obese	30 or more

a Use the formula BMI $= \dfrac{w}{h^2}$ to calculate your BMI.

It is not appropriate to use the formula BMI $= \dfrac{w}{h^2}$ for all body types. Athletes, for example, may have a high BMI because they are very muscular (muscles weigh more than fat).

b Investigate the formula BMI $= k \times \dfrac{w}{h^2}$ for different body types. Suggest values for k.

8 a p is inversely proportional to m.
   Given that $p = 1.3$ when $m = 5$, express p in terms of m.
   b Work out the value of p when $m = 26$.
   c Work out the value of m when $p = 0.25$.

9 a h is inversely proportional to the square root of t.
   Given that $h = 115$ when $t = 2.56$, express h in terms of t.
   b Work out the value of h when $t = 64$.
   c Work out the value of t when $h = 0.4$.

10 The resistance of a wire, R ohms, varies inversely as the square of its radius, t cm.
   Given that the resistance is 0.6 ohms when the radius is 0.4 cm,
   find the resistance when the radius is 0.3 cm.

11 T is inversely proportional to the cube root of r.
   Given that $T = 1.36$ when $r = 8$
   work out the value of r when $T = 6.8$.
   Give your answer correct to 3 significant figures.

12 The attraction force, F newtons, between two objects is inversely proportional to the square of the distance, d km, between them.
   Given that the attraction force between two bodies is 600 newtons when they are 300 km apart, find the distance apart of the same two objects when the attraction force between them is 800 newtons.
   Give your answer correct to 3 significant figures.

13 When $E = 10$, $v = 2$
When $E = 20$, $v = 4$
Kerry says that E is directly proportional to the square of v.
Is she correct?
You must give reasons for your answer.

14 When $x = \frac{1}{3}$, $y = 9$
When $x = 1$, $y = 4$
Ali says that x is inversely proportional to the square root of y.
Is he correct?
You must give reasons for your answer.

15 p is inversely proportional to t^3.
Given that $p = 8$ when $t = 3$, find the value of p when $t = 4$

16 The volume of a bottle is directly proportional to the cube of its width.
When the width of the bottle is 8 cm, the volume of the bottle is 100 cm³.
Work out the volume of the bottle when the width is 12 cm.

Challenge yourself

1 Some values of x and y are given in the table.
There is a proportional relationship between x and y.

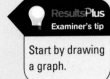
ResultsPlus
Examiner's tip

Start by drawing
a graph.

x	4	6	10
y	4	9	25

Find an equation that links x and y.

2 The table shows values of v and h.
There is a proportional relationship between v and h. Find an equation that links v and h.

v	2	4	5
h	10	$1\frac{1}{4}$	$\frac{16}{25}$

Unit 3 | 18 Transformations of functions

Key Points

- A function, $y = f(x)$, is a rule for working out values of y when given values of x.
- The curve $y = f(x) + a$ is a **translation** of a units parallel to the y axis or a translation by $\begin{pmatrix} 0 \\ a \end{pmatrix}$ of the curve $y = f(x)$.

  The curve $y = f(x + a)$ is a **translation** of $-a$ units parallel to the x-axis or a translation of $\begin{pmatrix} -a \\ 0 \end{pmatrix}$ of the curve $y = f(x)$.
- The curve $y = af(x)$ (where a is a constant) is a **stretch** of magnitude a parallel to the y-axis of the curve $y = f(x)$.
- The curve $y = f(ax)$ (where a is a constant) is a **stretch** of magnitude $\dfrac{1}{a}$ parallel to the x-axis of the curve $y = f(x)$.
- The curve $y = f(-x)$ is a **reflection in the y-axis** of the curve $y = f(x)$.
- The curve $y = -f(x)$ is a **reflection in the x-axis** of the curve $y = f(x)$.
- The curve $y = -f(-x)$ is a **rotation by 180° about the origin** of the curve $y = f(x)$.

Questions in this chapter are targeted at the grades indicated.

A03   A*

1   Here is the graph of $y = f(x) = x^2$.

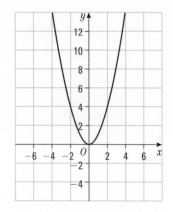

Draw the graphs of:

  i $y = f(x) + 2$ **ii** $y = f(x) - 5$ **iii** $y = f(x + 3)$ **iv** $y = f(x - 2)$

  v $y = 2f(x)$ **vi** $y = f(2x)$ **vii** $y = f\left(\dfrac{x}{2}\right)$ **viii** $y = -f(x)$

2   Here is a curve with equation $y = f(x)$.

The maximum point of the curve is $(2, 6)$.

Write down the coordinates of the maximum point of:

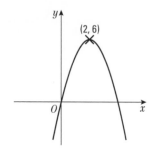

A03

  i $y = f(x) - 6$ **ii** $y = f(x - 2)$ **iii** $y = 3f(x)$

  iv $y = f(2x)$ **v** $y = f(-x)$

A*

A03

3 Describe the transformations which change the graph of $y = f(x)$ into

i $y = f(x) + 4$ ii $y = f(x) - 2$ iii $y = f(x - 5)$

iv $y = f(x + 7)$ v $y = 3f(x)$ vi $y = f(-x)$

vii $y = f(4x)$ viii $y = -f(x)$

A03

4 Here is the graph of $y = f(x) = \sin x$.

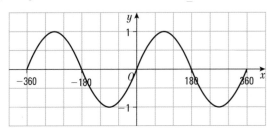

Hence, or otherwise, write down the equation of each of the following graphs.

a

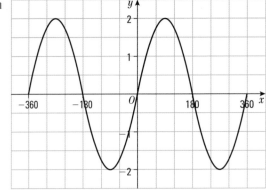

b

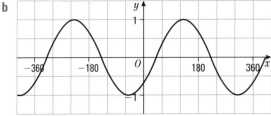

c

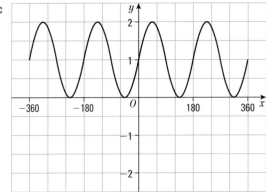

d

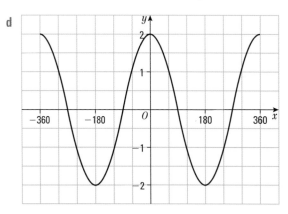

5 Here is the graph of $y = f(x)$.
   Sketch
   a $y = f(-x)$
   b $y = f(2x)$
   c Hence, or otherwise, sketch $y = f(-2x)$

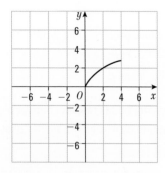

6 Here is the graph of $y = f(x)$.
   a Sketch the graph of $y = -f(x)$
   b Describe the transformation that maps the graph of
         $y = f(x)$ to the graph of $y = -f(x)$.
   c What is the image of the point $(3, 1)$ under this
         transformation?

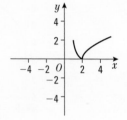

7 Here is the graph of the curve C_1 with equation $y = f(x)$.
   a Draw the curve C_2 with equation $y = f(0.5x)$.
   b Describe the transformation that maps C_1 to C_2.

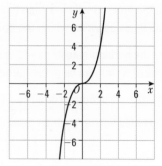

8 The graph of $y = f(x)$ is as shown in the previous question.
   a Sketch the graph of $y = f(x + 2)$.
   b Describe fully the transformation that maps $y = f(x)$ to $y = f(x + 2)$.
   The point (p, q) on $y = f(x)$ is mapped to the point $(0, 4)$ on $y = f(x + 2)$.
   c Find the values of p and q.

Challenge yourself

The rise and fall of the level of water in a harbour can be modelled using a sine function.

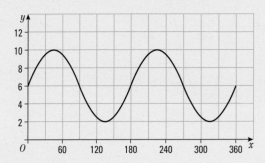

The equation of the above graph can be written as
$y = a\sin(bx) + c$.

a   Find the values of a, b and c.

One day a harbour master needs to know between which times it will be safe for a boat that requires at least 4 metres of water to be in the harbour. He uses the same graph but with the scale now representing the time of day.

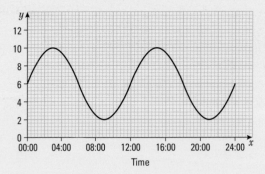

b   Write down the times at which: **i** high tide occurs, **ii** low tide occurs.
c   Work out the times between which the boat can safely be in the harbour.

One week later the harbour master needs to know the times between which a ship requiring at least 7 metres of water can be in the harbour.

However, high tide now occurs at 05 00 and 17 00.

d   Work out the times between which the ship can safely be in the harbour.

Unit 3 | 19 Area

🔍 Key Points

○ For a sector with angle $x°$ of a circle with radius r

sector $= \dfrac{x}{360}$ of the circle so

area of sector $= \dfrac{x}{360} \times \pi r^2$

and arc length $= \dfrac{x}{360} \times 2\pi r$

> You learnt to find perimeters and areas of shapes in Chapter 14, unit 2.

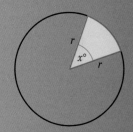

○ Total surface area of cone $= \pi r^2 + \pi r l$, where r is the radius and l is the slant height.

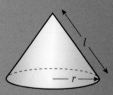

○ Surface area of sphere $= 4\pi r^2$, where r is the radius.

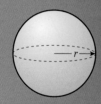

---

1 These shapes are made from sectors of circles. Calculate:
  i the perimeter   **ii** the area.
  Write your answer correct to 3 significant figures.

Questions in this chapter are targeted at the grades indicated.

a

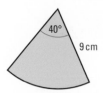

40° 9 cm

b

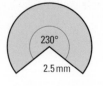

230° 2.5 mm

c

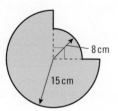

8 cm 15 cm

d

30° 5 mm 8 mm

e

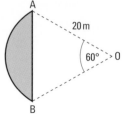

A 20 m 60° O B

2 For these solids, calculate the surface area, leaving your answers in terms of π where appropriate.

a

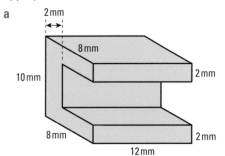

b

c

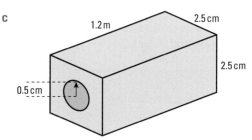

d

e

f

g

3 Calculate the area of the shaded segment.

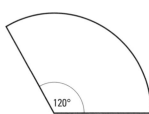

4 The area of this sector is $27\pi\,\text{cm}^2$.

a Find the radius of the sector.

b Find, in terms of π, the arc length of the sector.

c Find the radius of a circle with circumference the same as this arc length.

5 The radius of the circle is **15 cm**.
The angle of the sector is **150°**.

Calculate the area of the sector.
Give your answer in terms of π.

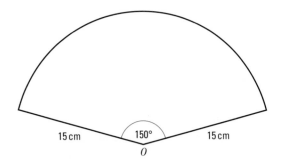

15 cm   150°   15 cm

O

6 Calculate the surface area of a hexagonal prism of side 3 cm and length 10 cm.

AO2
AO3

7 The radius of a circle is **10 cm**.
A sector of the circle has an arc length of **10 cm**.
a Work out the size of the angle of the sector.
b Work out the area of the sector.

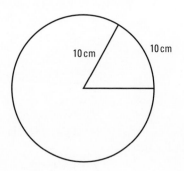

10 cm   10 cm

AO2
AO3

8 The area of a sector of a circle is **75.4 cm²**.
The radius of the circle is **12 cm**.
Calculate the length of the arc of the sector.

AO2
AO3

Challenge yourself

a Calculate the area of paper used to make this witch's hat (assume there are no overlaps).

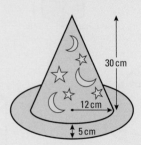

30 cm

12 cm

5 cm

b Estimate the number of hats that can be made from a roll of paper 50 m by 1 m.

AO2
AO3

Unit 3 | 20 Volume

Key Points

○ Volume of pyramid $= \frac{1}{3} \times$ area of base $\times$ vertical height

○ Volume of cone $= \frac{1}{3} \times$ area of base $\times$ vertical height

$$= \frac{1}{3}\pi r^2 h$$

where r is the radius and h is the height.

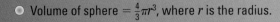

○ Volume of sphere $= \frac{4}{3}\pi r^3$, where r is the radius.

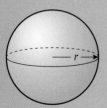

○ Volume of cylinder $= \pi r^2 h$
where r is the radius and h is the height.

A

Questions in this chapter are targeted at the grades indicated.

**A02
A03**

1   For each solid, calculate the volume, correct to 3 significant figures.

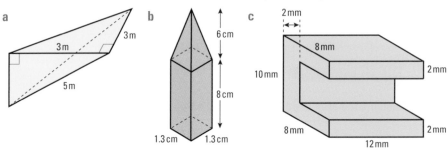

a   3 m   5 m   3 m

b   6 cm   8 cm   1.3 cm   1.3 cm

c   2 mm   8 mm   10 mm   2 mm   8 mm   12 mm   2 mm

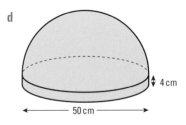

d   4 cm   50 cm

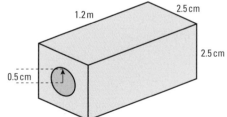

e   1.2 m   2.5 cm   2.5 cm   0.5 cm

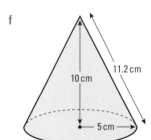

f   11.2 cm   10 cm   5 cm

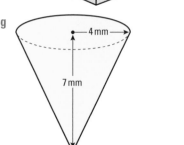

g   4 mm   7 mm

h 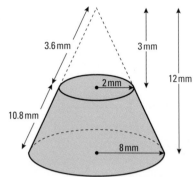   **i**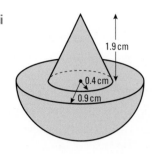

2 A spherical ball has a diameter of 45 cm. Work out the volume of the ball.

3 A cylinder has base radius x cm and
height $4x$ cm.
A cone has base radius x cm and
height h cm.
The volume of the cylinder and the
volume of the cone are equal.
Find h in terms of x.
Give your answer in its simplest form.

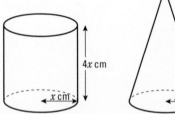

4 **a** Find the radius of a sphere with volume 100 cm³.

  b The surface area in cm² and volume in cm³ of a sphere are the same.
       Calculate its radius.

5 Calculate the volume of a hexagonal prism of side 3 cm and length 10 cm.

> **Challenge yourself**

This is harder than anything you will encounter in the exam, but the underlying maths is covered in your
GCSE course. Have a go and see how you do.

The vertex of each pyramid is above the centre of the base.
Find the angle x.

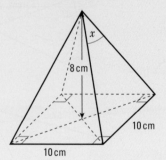   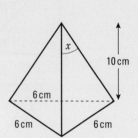

Unit 3 | 21 Congruence and similarity

🔍 Key Points

- Two triangles are congruent if they have the same sides (size) and the the the same angles.

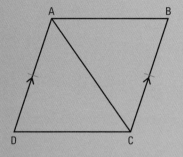

- Two triangles are similar if they have the same angles or corresponding sides are in the same ratio (one triangle is an enlargement of the other) or they have one equal angle and the adjacent sides are in the same ratio

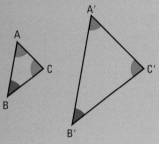

Questions in this chapter are targeted at the grades indicated.

1 ABCD is a parallelogram.

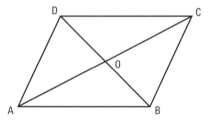

a Prove that triangle ABC is congruent to triangle CDA.

b Find a triangle that is congruent to triangle AOD.
Prove that they are congruent. Give reasons for your working.

2 Two of these triangles are congruent. Which two? Explain your answer.

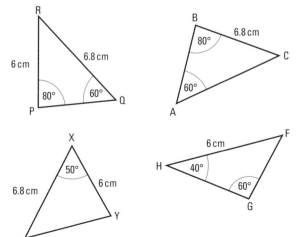

3 Two of these triangles are similar. Which two? Explain your answer.

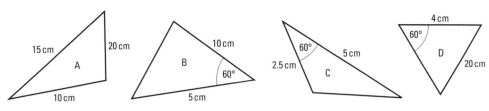

You may need
to rotate and/
or flip a shape
to match angles
and sides

4 Triangle ABC is similar to triangle XYZ.
   Calculate the length of:
   a AB
   b YZ.

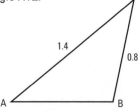

5

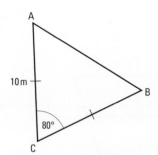

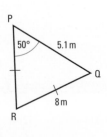

   a Why is triangle ABC similar to triangle PQR?
   b Find the length of AB.

6 BCE and ACD are straight lines.

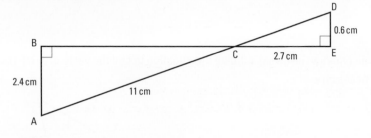

   a Prove that the two triangles are similar.
   b Use similar triangles to find the length of:
      i CD   ii BC.

7 a Prove that triangle TUX is similar to triangle VWX.
   b Find the lengths of: i VW   ii UW.

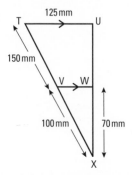

A03

A03

A02
A03

A02
A03

A02
A03

A*
A02
A03

8 ABC is a straight line.
Find two triangles that are similar.
Give reasons for your answer.

Find the missing
angles first.

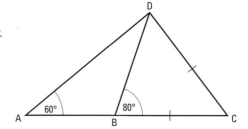

A02
A03

9 Calculate the missing sides
using similar triangles.

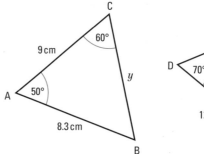
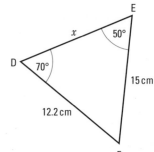

10 ABCD is a parallelogram.
ABCD is similar to CFED.
Calculate the length of CF.

Sketch the
two similar
parallelograms
side by side

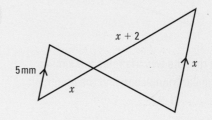

Challenge yourself

Use similar triangles to find an equation involving x. Solve the equation to find the value of x, correct to
3 significant figures, where necessary.

1
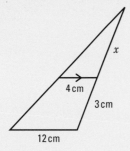

2
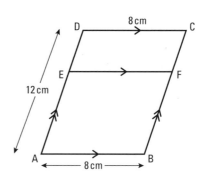

3
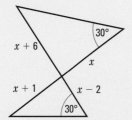

4
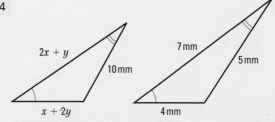

Unit 3 | 22 Circle geometry

Key Points

○ You should know and be able to apply the following theorems:

   ⊙ The tangents to a circle from a point outside the circle are equal in length and equally inclined to the line joining the point to the centre of the circle.

See section 13.8 in Unit 2

   ⊙ The angle between the tangent and the radius is a right angle.

   ⊙ The angle in a semicircle is a right angle.

   ⊙ The angle subtended by a chord at the centre is twice the angle subtended by the chord at the circumference.

   ⊙ Angles subtended at the circumference by the same chord or equal chords are equal.

   ⊙ The opposite angles of a cyclic quadrilateral are supplementary (add up to 180°).

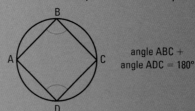

angle ABC + angle ADC = 180°

   ⊙ The alternate segment theorem (angle DAB = angle ACB).

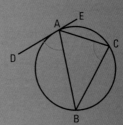

---

1 The diagram shows a circle, centre O.

   PS and PT are tangents to the circle at S and T, respectively.

   SOR is a diameter.

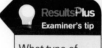

Diagram NOT accurately drawn

   Q is the point such that RTQ is a straight line and QP is parallel to RS.

   Angle SPT = 50°.

   Work out the size of angle PQT

Questions in this chapter are targeted at the grades indicated.

A **A02**

ResultsPlus
Examiner's tip

What type of triangle is PST?

2 O is the centre of the circle.

   AB = BC

   Angle AOC = 124°

   Work out the size of angle OCB.

A02

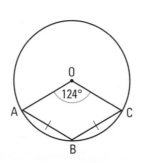

Diagram NOT accurately drawn

A

3 In the diagram, O is the centre of the circle.
P, Q, R and S are points on the circle.
Angle ROP = 115°
Calculate the size of angle RSP.

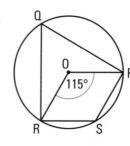

Diagram NOT
accurately drawn

A03

ResultsPlus
Examiners tip

Join O to C and
use the angle
properties
of isosceles
triangles.

*4 O is the centre of the circle.

AOB is a diameter.

Prove, without using any circle
theorems, that angle ACB is a
right angle.

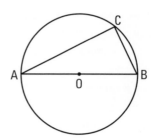

Diagram NOT
accurately drawn

A*
A03

5 O is the centre of the circle. XOY and AOB are diameters.

Angle AOY = 90°.

XZW and BYW are straight lines.

a Calculate the size of angle
ZWY.

Give reasons for your answer.

b Show that $XW^2 = BY^2 + BW^2$.

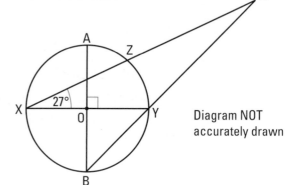

Diagram NOT
accurately drawn

A02
A03

*6 O is the centre of the circle.

Calculate the size of the angle
marked x.

Give reasons for your answer.

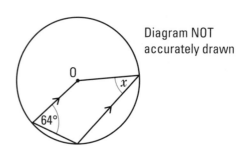

Diagram NOT
accurately drawn

A03

*7 A, B and E are three points on a circle.

BD is the tangent to the
circle at B.

BEC and AED are straight
lines.

AC is parallel to BD.

a Prove that angle
ABE = angle BAC.

b Prove that triangle ACE is similar to triangle ABD.

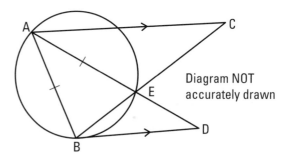

Diagram NOT
accurately drawn

A*
A03

* 8 A, B and C are three points on a circle such that triangle ABC is equilateral.

P is a point on the circle.

The straight line PCQ meets the line through B parallel to AP.

Prove that triangle BPQ is equilateral.

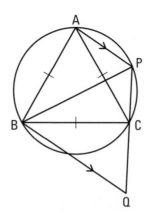

Diagram NOT accurately drawn

A03

* 9 A, B, C and D are points on a circle. APC, BPD, BAQ and CDQ are straight lines.

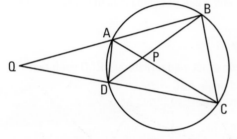

Diagram NOT accurately drawn

ResultsPlus
Examiner's tip

Use angles in the same segment in both parts.

  a i Prove that triangle APB is similar to triangle DPC.
     ii Hence, prove that AP × CP = DP × BP.
  b Prove that QA × QB = QD × QC.

▶ **Challenge yourself**

Ptolemy's theorem
A, B, C and D are four points on a circle.
E is the point on AC such that angle EBC = angle ABD.

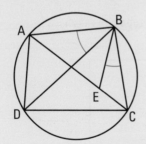

  a Prove that triangle ABE is similar to triangle CBD.
  b Prove that triangle BEC is similar to triangle ABD.
Hence prove Ptolemy's theorem
AB × CD + BC × DA = AC × BD.

Unit 3 | 23 Constructions and loci

Key Points

- Using ruler and compasses you can:
  - construct the perpendicular bisector of a line segment.
  - construct the perpendicular to a line from an external point or from an internal point.
  - construct the bisector of an angle.
- The locus of a point is the set of all points which obey a mathematical rule.

See section 14.2

See section 14.3

See section 14.4

A

A03

Questions in this chapter are targeted at the grades indicated.

1 Draw a circle of radius 5 cm. Use ruler and a pair of compasses to construct a regular octagon with all vertices on the circle.

2 Use ruler and a pair of compasses to construct a quadrilateral ABCD such that AB = BC = 8cm, CD = BD = 6 cm and angle ABC = 75°.

3

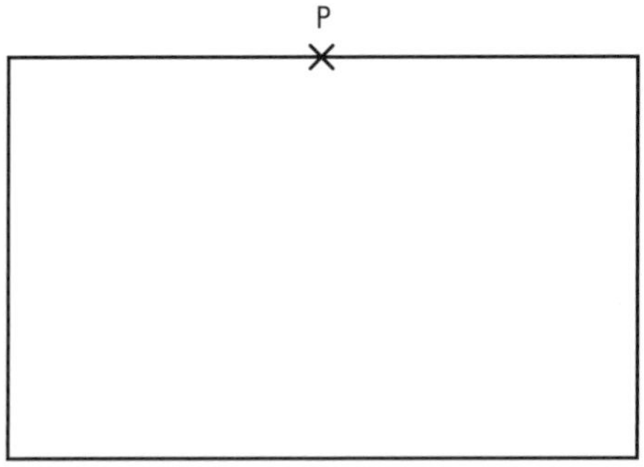

The diagram represents the plan of a building which is 8m wide and 5 m long. P is the point on the ground 4m from a corner. A rope of length 7m is attached to the point P.

a Draw an accurate scale diagram to show the region outside the building that the rope can reach.

b Calculate the area of the region that the rope can reach.

4

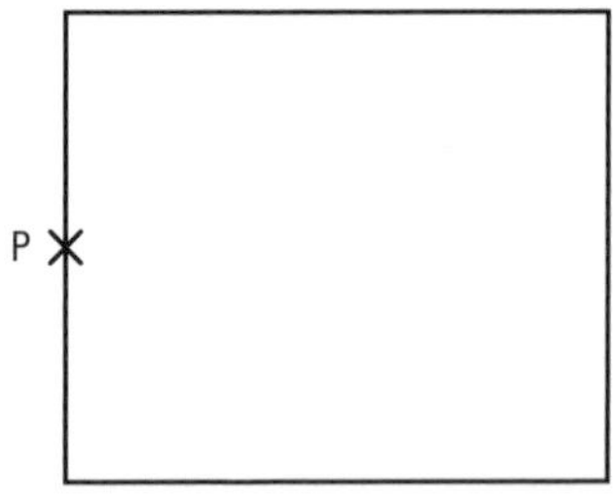

The diagram represents the plan of a building which is a square of side 4 m. P is the point on the ground 2m from a corner. A rope of length 8m is attached to P.

a Draw an accurate scale diagram to show the region outside the building that the rope can reach.

b Calculate the area of the region that the rope can reach.

5

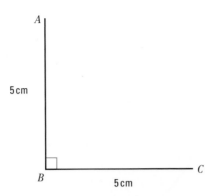

A piece of wire of length 10 is bent into the shape of a right angle ABC.
AB = BC = 5 cm.

a   Draw the locus of all points which are exactly 2 cm from the wire.

b   Calculate the length of the locus.

* **6**   OD, OE and OF are the perpendicular
bisectors of the sides BC, CA and AB of
the triangle ABC.

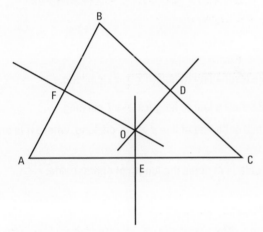

Explain why a circle can be drawn
through the points A, B and C.

ResultsPlus
Examiner's tip   A03

What
geometrical
property have
all points on a
perpendicular
bisector?

7   The altitude of a triangle is a line from a vertex
to the opposite side meeting it at right angles.

Construct the three altitudes of triangle PQR.
Show that they all pass through the same point.

A03

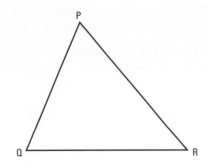

A☆

* **8** In triangle PQR, the bisector of angle QPR and the bisector of angle QRP meet at I.

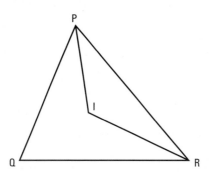

a Show that I is equidistant from the sides PR, RQ and QP.

b Show that IQ bisects angle PQR.

Challenge yourself

a Here is a line x cm long.

A ———————————————— B

Explain how, using ruler and compasses, you can construct a line of length $x \times \sqrt{7}$ cm long.

b Explain how, using ruler and compasses, you can construct a line of length $x \times \sqrt{7}$ cm long.

c Explain how, using ruler and compasses, you can construct a line of line $x \times \sqrt{n}$ cm long, where n is an integer.

d A golden rectangle is one in which the length of one side is $\varnothing$ times the length of another side.

$$\varnothing = \frac{1 + \sqrt{5}}{2}$$

Starting with a line of length 1 unit, show how a line of length $\varnothing$ can be constructed.

Regular polygons with number of sides given by $m = 2^{2^{n}} + 1$ where m is prime can be drawn with ruler and compasses.

e Work out the values of m when $n = 0, 1, 2, 3, 4$.

f Show that 641 is a factor of m when $n = 5$.

Unit 3 | 24 Transformations

🔍 Key Points

◉ One transformation followed by another can often be described in terms of a single transformation.

◉ A translation is best described by using a vector.

◉ A rotation is described by stating the centre, the sense and the size of the angle.

◉ An enlargement is described by stating the centre and the scale factor.

◉ A reflection is described by stating the line of reflection.

◉ To study the effects of a combination of transformations it is useful to draw a right-angled triangle with height 4 units and base 2 units.

1 Enlarge shape A, centre O, scale factor 2 to give shape B.

Questions in this chapter are targeted at the grades indicated.

A

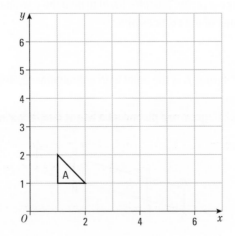

Shape B is enlarged by scale factor 0.5, centre (k, k) to give shape C.
Describe fully the transformation that will map shape A to shape C.

2 A shape X is reflected in the line $x = p$ to give the shape Y.
The shape Y is reflected in the line $x = q$ to give the shape Z
Describe fully the single transformation that will map X to Y.

A03

3 P is the point (a, b)
Q is the image of P under a reflection in the line $y - 2x = 0$
R is the image of Q under a reflection in the line $2y + x = 0$.
Describe fully the single transformation that will map P to R.

A02

4 L_1 and L_2 are perpendicular straight lines which intersect at O. Q is the image of P under the reflection in the line L_1. R is the image of Q in the line L_2.

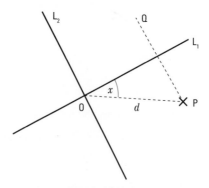

Show that POR is a straight line and that OP = OR.

5 The coordinates of the vertices of the triangle T are (p, p), (p, q) and (r, p).
T is enlarged by scale factor 2, centre (a, b) to give the triangle S.
Find the coordinates of the vertices of S.

6 ABCD is a parallelogram. A is the point with coordinates (2, 3) and B is the point with coordinates (4, 9).
Copies of the parallelogram are placed next to each other as in the diagram.

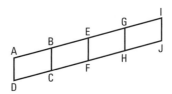

The point A can be translated to the point J with the vector $\begin{pmatrix} 9 \\ 22 \end{pmatrix}$

Find the coordinates of the point D.

7 Shape T is rotated by 180° about the point (3, 0) to give shape U.

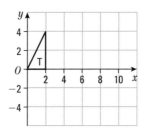

Shape U is rotated by 180° about the point (6, 0) to give shape V.

a Describe fully the single transformation that will map shape T to shape V.

The shape A is rotated by 180° about $(p, 0)$ to give the shape B. B is rotated by 180° about $(q, 0)$ to give the shape C.

b Describe fully the single transformation that will map shape A to shape C.

8   Shape T is rotated by 90° clockwise about the point (3, 0) to give shape U.

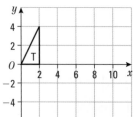

Shape U is rotated by 90° anticlockwise about the point (6, 0) to give shape V.

a   Describe fully the single transformation that will map shape T to shape V.

The shape A is rotated by 90° clockwise about (*p*, 0) to give the shape B. B is rotated by 90° anticlockwise about (*q*, 0) to give the shape C.

b   Describe fully the single transformation that will map shape A to shape C.

> **Challenge yourself**

This is harder than anything you will encounter in the exam, but the underlying maths is covered in your GCSE course. Have a go and see how you do.

Animated transformations
The basis of all computer animations uses the transformations studied in Chapter 15.

a   Translate shape T using the vector $\begin{pmatrix} 2t \\ 0 \end{pmatrix}$ for values of *t* from 0 to 4.

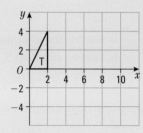

Describe what happens to shape T.

What would be the effect of the vector $\begin{pmatrix} 2t \\ 2t \end{pmatrix}$?

b   Enlarge shape U with scale factor 1.5*t*, centre (5, 7) for values of *t* = 1, 1.5, 2, 2.5, 3.

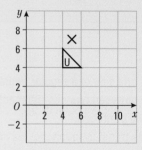

Describe what happens to shape U.

What would be the effect of a scale factor of 0.5*t*?

Unit 3 | 25 Pythagoras' Theorem and trigonometry 1

Key Points

● Pythagoras' Theorem states that:
in a right-angled triangle, the square of the hypotenuse is
equal to the sum of the squares of the other two sides.

$c^2 = a^2 + b^2$

or

$AB^2 = BC^2 + CA^2$

where AB^2 means the length of the side AB squared.

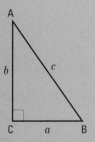

● The terms **sine** (sin), **cosine** (cos) and **tangent** (tan) are called trigonometric ratios,
or trig ratios.

$$\sin x° = \frac{\text{opp}}{\text{hyp}} \qquad \cos x° = \frac{\text{adj}}{\text{hyp}} \qquad \tan x° = \frac{\text{opp}}{\text{adj}}$$

SOHCAHTOA might help you remember these results.

A
AO2
AO3

Questions in
this chapter are
targeted at the
grades indicated.

1 Jane's kite is on the end of a 60 m string at point A on the
ground on a bearing of 070°.

The kite lands at point B, 60 m from Jane on a bearing of 150°.

a Draw a diagram.
b How far   **i** east   **ii** south is the kite from Jane?
c Calculate the   **i** distance   **ii** bearing of A from B.

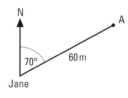

A✩
AO2
AO3

2 This set square has a 20 cm ruler along one edge. Calculate the total perimeter.

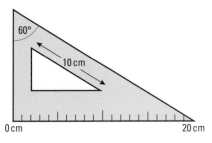

AO2
AO3

3 **a** Calculate the length of one side of a regular pentagon of radius 6 cm.
b Calculate the distance between two non-adjacent vertices.
c Calculate the area of the pentagon.

4   The diagram shows a fold-up stool with a cloth seat
    and metal frame.
    a Calculate the height of the seat.
    b Calculate the total length of the metal used in the frame.

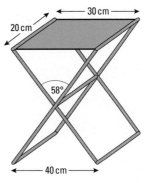

5   Find the mssing sides and angles of these triangles.

a 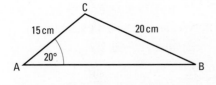   b 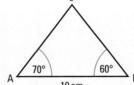   c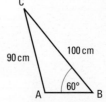

6   a Draw a scalene triangle large enough so that you can measure the angles and sides.
    b Use trigonometry to find the angles.
    c Check your answers by measuring the angles.

Challenge yourself

1   As well as degrees (°), angles can be measured in radians (ᶜ). You can convert between radians and
    degrees using the equation $360° = 2\pi^c$.
    a Convert the following to degrees   i 0.3^c ii 1.5^c iii $\frac{\pi^c}{4}$

    b Convert the following to radians   i $60°$ ii $24°$ iii $220°$

2   An approximate value of $\sin x$ can be found using the formula $\sin x \approx x - \frac{x^3}{6} + \frac{x^5}{120}$.
    This formula only works when the angle x is measured in radians.
    Use the formula to estimate the value of the following angles.

    a   i 1.2^c ii 0.75^c iii $\frac{\pi^c}{6}$
    b   i $45°$ ii $72°$ iii $130°$

3   What do you notice about the accuracy of your approximations as x increases?

4   The formula for $\sin x$ is the first three terms of the series
$$\sin x = x - \frac{x^3}{3 \times 2 \times 1} + \frac{x^5}{5 \times 4 \times 3 \times 2 \times 1} \cdots$$

    a Write down the next term in the series to obtain a more accurate formula for sin x.
    b Use the new formula to estimate sin 130° again.
    c How accurate is the estimate now?

5   Extend the formula for $\sin x$ until it gives 4 decimal places of accuracy for sin 130°.

Unit 3 | 26 Pythagoras' Theorem and trigonometry 2

🔍 **Key Points**

○ Graph of $y = \sin \theta$

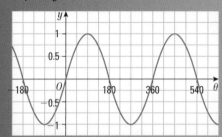

○ The graph of $y = \sin \theta$:
  ○ cuts the θ-axis at ...,
    $-180, 0, 180, 360, 540, ...$
  ○ repeats itself every 360°, that is,
    it has a **period** of 360°
  ○ has a maximum value of 1 at
    $\theta = ..., 90, 450, ...$
  ○ has a minimum value of -1 at
    $\theta = ..., -90, 270, ...$

○ Graph of $y = \cos \theta$

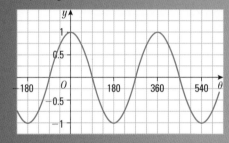

○ The graph of $y = \cos \theta$:
  ○ cuts the θ-axis at ..., $-90, 90, 270,$
    $450, ...$
  ○ repeats itself every 360°, that is it
    has a **period** of 360°
  ○ has a maximum value of 1 at
    $\theta = ..., 0, 360, ...$
  ○ has a minimum value of -1 at
    $\theta = ..., -180, 180, 540, ...$

> You learnt about Pythagoras' theorem and trigonometry for right-angled triangles in Chapter 16

○ Area of a triangle $= \frac{1}{2}ab\sin C$

○ Sine Rule: $\dfrac{\sin A}{a} = \dfrac{\sin B}{b} = \dfrac{\sin C}{c}$

○ Cosine Rule: $a^2 = b^2 + c^2 - 2bc\cos A$ and $\cos A = \dfrac{b^2 + c^2 - a^2}{2bc}$

A
AO2
AO3

Questions in this chapter are targeted at the grades indicated.

1 The diagrams show three different pencil cases.
  i Calculate the longest pencil that will fit into each pencil case.
  ii Find the angle this pencil makes with the base of the pencil case.

 ResultsPlus
Examiner's tip

Draw right-angled triangles involving the lengths and angles you need to find.

a

b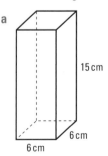

c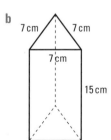

2 Solve the equations, correct to 1 decimal place.

a $\sin x = 0.8$, $0° \leqslant x \leqslant 360°$

b $\cos\theta = \frac{1}{4}$, $-180° \leqslant \theta \leqslant 180°$

c $3\cos\theta = 0.8$, $0° \leqslant \theta \leqslant 360°$

> **ResultsPlus**
> **Examiner's tip**
>
> Sketch the graph of sine and cosine for the given range.

3 i Use the sine and cosine rules to find the missing sides and angles.

ii Calculate the area of each triangle.

a
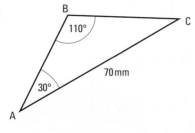

b
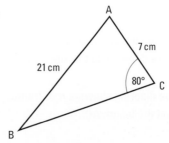

c
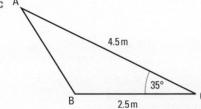

d
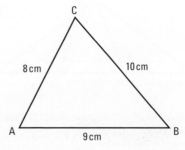

e
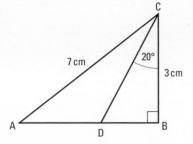

4 The boat is held fast by two anchors. The angle between the anchor chains is 126.4°. The anchor point on the boat is 10 m above the seabed.

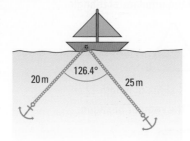

a Find the distance between the anchors.

b Find the angle each chain makes with the seabed (assuming that the seabed is horizontal).

5 The angle of elevation of the kite from the man on the cliff is 50°. The angle of depression of the boy from the man is 30°.

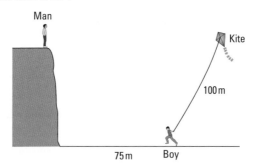

a Find the distance of the boy from the man.

b Find the angle the kite string makes with the ground.

6 The diagram shows a roof frame.
Find the length AB.

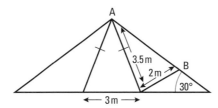

7 The sides of a triangular field measure 250 m, 190 m and 320 m.

a Calculate the area of the field.

A straight fence from the corner of the two shorter sides divides the field into two equal areas.

b Calculate the length of the fence.

* **8** Work out the area of the parallelogram.

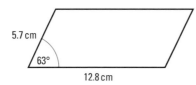

* **9** **a** An equilateral triangle has sides of length 12 cm.
Calculate the area of the equilateral triangle.

b A regular hexagon has sides of length 12 cm.
Calculate the area of the regular hexagon.

Challenge yourself

The angle between two planes is the angle between two lines perpendicular to the line where the planes meet (see angle between dotted lines).

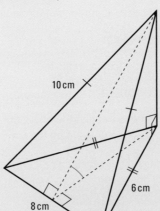

10 cm

6 cm

8 cm

1   Calculate the angle between the two planes containing the isosceles triangles in the diagram above.

2   Calculate the angles between the sloping faces of
   a   a right equilateral triangular pyramid (tetrahedron)

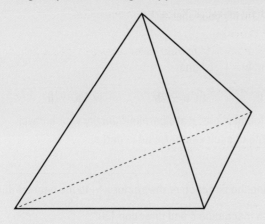

   b   a right square pyramid, whose edges are all 10 cm long.

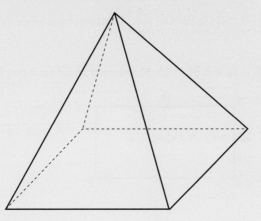

Unit 3 | 27 Vectors

🔍 Key Points

You learnt about Pythagoras' theorem and trigonometry in Chapter 16.

- The magnitude of the vector $\begin{pmatrix} x \\ y \end{pmatrix}$ is $\sqrt{x^2 + y^2}$.

- Triangle law of vector addition states that $\overrightarrow{PQ} + \overrightarrow{QR} = \overrightarrow{PR}$.

- When $\overrightarrow{PQ} = \mathbf{a}$, $\overrightarrow{QP} = -\mathbf{a}$.

- When $\overrightarrow{PQ} = k\overrightarrow{RS}$ and k is a scalar (number), the lines PQ and RS are parallel and the length of PQ is k times the length of RS.

- When $\overrightarrow{PQ} = k\overrightarrow{PR}$ then the lines PQ and PR are parallel. But these lines have the point P in common so that PQ and PR are part of the same straight line. That is, the points P, Q and R lie on the same straight line.

A
AO2 AO3

Questions in this chapter are targeted at the grades indicated.

1 a On squared paper, plot the points A(3, 1), B(7, 3), C(5, 7).

   b Find the vectors   i $\overrightarrow{AB}$ ii $\overrightarrow{BC}$

   c If $\overrightarrow{CD} = \begin{pmatrix} -4 \\ -2 \end{pmatrix}$ find the coordinates of D and plot the point.

   d What can you say about the lines AB and CD? Use vectors to justify your answer.

   e What shape is ABCD? Justify your answer.

AO2 AO3

2 a Given that $\mathbf{a} = \begin{pmatrix} 2 \\ 1 \end{pmatrix}$ and $\mathbf{b} = \begin{pmatrix} -2 \\ -2 \end{pmatrix}$ find:

      i $\mathbf{a} + \mathbf{b}$ ii $2\mathbf{a} + \mathbf{b}$ iii $\mathbf{a} - 2\mathbf{b}$ iv $3\mathbf{a} - \frac{1}{2}\mathbf{b}$ v $\mathbf{a} + \frac{1}{2}\mathbf{b}$

   b Which of the vectors found in part **a** are parallel? Justify your answer.

   c Calculate the magnitude of each vector found in part **a**.

AO2 AO3

3 a Use trigonometry to find the direction of the vector $\begin{pmatrix} 2 \\ 1 \end{pmatrix}$ to the nearest degree.

   b i Sketch a vector with magnitude 5 and direction 130°.
       ii Use trigonometry to write this as a column vector.

   c Write down two vectors that are parallel to $\begin{pmatrix} 3 \\ 4 \end{pmatrix}$ and that have twice its magnitude.

AO2 AO3

4 ABCD is a rectangle. AB = 6**a** and BC = 6**b**. M is a point on CD such that MC = $\frac{1}{3}$DC.

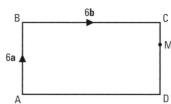

a Find, in terms of **a** and **b**, the vectors: i $\overrightarrow{MC}$ ii $\overrightarrow{AM}$.

The line BC is extended to the point N such that CN = 3**b**.

b Find the vector $\overrightarrow{MN}$.

c State a fact about points A, M and N.

5   ABCD is a quadrilateral.

A is the point (1, 2), B is the point (3, 6) and P is the midpoint of AB.

a Write down the coordinates of P.

C is the point (7, 4) and Q is the midpoint of BC.

b Write down the coordinates of Q.

D is the point (7, 2) and R is the midpoint of CD.

c Write down the coordinates of R.

S is the midpoint of AD.

d Write down the coordinates of S.

e Find the column vectors   i $\overrightarrow{PQ}$ ii $\overrightarrow{SR}$.

f Explain with reasons what the answers to **e** show about the quadrilateral PQRS.

6   OABC is a parallelogram.

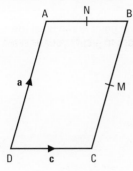

Diagram NOT
accurately drawn

M is the midpoint of CB.

N is the midpoint of AB.

$\overrightarrow{OA} = $ **a** $\overrightarrow{OC} = $ **c**

a Find, in terms of **a** and/or **c**, the vector $\overrightarrow{MB}$.

b Show that CA is parallel to MN.

7   AB = 2**a** + 3**b** and AM = **a** + 2**b**.

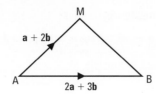

a Find the vector $\overrightarrow{BM}$ in terms of **a** and **b**.

Lines AM and BM are extended to points C and D such that AC = 4AM and BD = 4BM.

b Find, in terms of **a** and **b**, the vectors: i $\overrightarrow{MC}$ ii $\overrightarrow{MD}$ iii $\overrightarrow{DC}$.

c What can you say about the lines AB and DC? Give a reason for your answer.

8 **a** Find vectors: **i** $\overrightarrow{AB}$ **ii** $\overrightarrow{DE}$

b What can you say about lines AB and DE?
Give a reason for your answer.

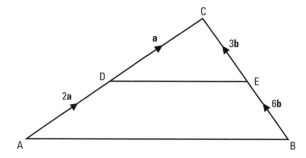

P is a point on AB such that DP is parallel to CB.

c Find the vector $\overrightarrow{DP}$.

A02
A03

Challenge yourself

1 Fixed point A has position vector $\overrightarrow{OA} = \begin{pmatrix} 2 \\ 3 \end{pmatrix}$.

On squared paper, draw a pair of axes, both numbered from 0 to 10. Plot the point A and label the position vector as **a**.

2 If $AB = \begin{pmatrix} 1 \\ 1 \end{pmatrix}$, plot the point B. Label the vector $\overrightarrow{AB}$ as **d**.

3 Write the position vector of B in terms of **a** and **d**.

4 **a** Plot the points whose position vectors are
a + 2**d**, **a** + 3**d**, **a** + 4**d**, **a** + 5**d**.
b What do you notice about the points?
c Where do you think the point **a** − 2**d** would be?
d Join the points using a straight line.

5 **a** What can you say about any point P whose position vector is
a + λ**d**, where λ is a number?
b If the position vector of P is called **r**, write down an equation for **r**.
This is the *vector equation* of the straight line.

6 **a** Draw a new pair of axes, numbered from 0 to 10.
b Draw the line with vector equation **r** = **a** + λ**d**, where **a** = $\begin{pmatrix} 9 \\ 1 \end{pmatrix}$ and **d** = $\begin{pmatrix} -2 \\ 2 \end{pmatrix}$.

7 Find a vector equation for the line joining A(3, 4) and B(5, 5).

Published by Pearson Education Limited, a company incorporated in England and Wales, having its registered office at Edinburgh Gate, Harlow, Essex, CM20 2JE. Registered company number: 872828

Edexcel is a registered trademark of Edexcel Limited

First published 2010

13 12 11 10
10 9 8 7 6 5 4 3 2 1

British Library Cataloguing in Publication Data
A catalogue record for this book is available from the British Library.

ISBN 978 1 84690676 3

Typeset by Tech-Set Ltd, Gateshead
Printed in Great Britain at Scotprint, Haddington

Disclaimer
This material has been published on behalf of Edexcel and offers high-quality support for the delivery of Edexcel qualifications.
This does not mean that the material is essential to achieve any Edexcel qualification, nor does it mean that it is the only suitable material available to support any Edexcel qualification. Edexcel material will not be used verbatim in setting any Edexcel examination or assessment. Any resource lists produced by Edexcel shall include this and other appropriate resources.

Copies of official specifications for all Edexcel qualifications may be found on the Edexcel website: www.edexcel.com